# *Exploring*
# EARTH AND SPACE SCIENCE

# 6

## LIG–MET

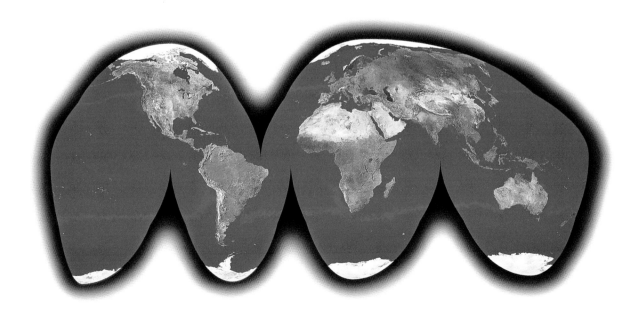

**Marshall Cavendish**
New York • London • Toronto • Sydney

## MARSHALL CAVENDISH CORPORATION

**Project editor:** Peter Mavrikis

**Editorial director:** Paul Bernabeo

## BROWN PARTWORKS

**Managing editor:** Anne O'Daly

**Project editors:** Caroline Beattie,
Lesley Campbell-Wright, Tom Jackson

**Design:** Richard Berry, Colin Woodman

**Picture researchers:** Liz Clachan,
Brenda Clynch

**Subeditors:** Jane Scarsbrook,
Chris Wiegand

**Marshall Cavendish Corporation**
99 White Plains Road
Tarrytown, New York 10591

Website: www.marshallcavendish.com

© 2002 Marshall Cavendish Corporation

Created by **Brown Partworks Limited**

**Library of Congress Cataloging-in-Publication Data**

Exploring earth and space science.
    p.  cm.
   Includes bibliographical references and indexes.
   Contents: 1. Acid and base-Calcium -- 2. Calendar-Continental shelf -- 3. Copper-El
Niño and La Niña -- 4. Energy-Gondwana -- 5. Grassland-Laser -- 6. Light-Meteor -- 7.
Meteorology-Ordovician period -- 8. Ore-Prospecting -- 9. Protein-Star -- 10.
Stratosphere-X ray -- 11. Index.
   ISBN 0-7614-7219-3 (set) -- ISBN 0-7614-7220-7 (v. 1) -- ISBN 0-7614-7221-5 (v. 2)
-- ISBN 0-7614-7222-3 (v. 3) -- ISBN 0-7614-7223-1 (v. 4) -- ISBN 0-7614-7224-X (v.
5) -- ISBN 0-7614-7225-8 (v. 6) -- ISBN 0-7614-7226-6 (v. 7) -- ISBN 0-7614-7227-4
(v. 8) -- ISBN 0-7614-7228-2 (v. 9) -- ISBN 0-7614-7229-0 (v. 10) -- ISBN
0-7614-7230-4 (v. 11)
   1. Earth sciences--Encyclopedias. 2. Space sciences--Encyclopedias. 3.
Astronomy--Encyclopedias

QE5 .E96 2002

550'.3--dc21

                                      00-065801

                                           CIP

                                           AC

**ISBN 0-7614-7219-3 (set)**

**ISBN 0-7614-7225-8 (vol. 6)**

Printed in Hong Kong

06 05 04 03 02 01 00  5 4 3 2 1

## PHOTOGRAPHIC CREDITS

**Bureau International des Poids et Mesures:** *450*
**Image Bank:** *456*, Chris Coles *452*, Peter Hendrie *426–27*, Jeff Hunter *443*, Eric Meola *404–5*
**Mary Evans Picture Library:** *433*
**NASA:** *423, 424–25, 448, 460, 462–63, 464, 465*, Neil A. Armstrong *422*, David R. Scott *421*
**NOAA:** C. Clark *408*, Reese *441*
**Science Photo Library:** *405, 442*, European Space Agency *440*, BP / NRSC *438*, Institute of
Oceanographic Sciences / NERC *437*, Novosti Press Agency *449*, Alex Bartel *436*, George Bernard
*474–75*, Dr. Jeremy Burgess *417–18*, Chris Butler *466*, Ron Church *444*, Martin Dohrn *414*, Simon
Fraser *410*, Fundamental Photos *434*, David Guyon *469*, Davis Hart *457*, Aaron Haupt *418*, Jan
Hinsch *406*, Steve Horrell *412–13*, Russ Lappa *471*, Peter Menzel *478*, NASA *435, 445, 446*, Alfred
Pasieka *411*, John Sandford *477*, Sinclair Stammers *431*, Kaj R. Svensson *468*, David Taylor *428–29*,
Charles D. Winters *458–59*, Frank Zullo *476*
**Trip:** S. Grant *432*, B. Needle *470*, H. Rogers *416, 435*
**Werner Foreman:** Christian Deydier *472–73*

**Front cover:** Cave in the side of an iceberg (Corbis, Peter Johnson)

**Title page:** Projection of Earth's land and oceans (Science Photo Library, Worldsat
                International and J. Knighton)

**Back cover:** The water cycle (Marshall Cavendish)

# *Exploring*

# EARTH AND SPACE SCIENCE

# 6

## LIG–MET

**Marshall Cavendish**
New York • London • Toronto • Sydney

# Light

**A range of wavelengths, between red and violet, that is visible to the human eye**

Without light from the Sun, life on Earth could not exist. In addition, the ability to detect the presence or absence of light shapes the way humans see the world.

Light is electromagnetic radiation that moves in waves of energy at 186,282 miles per second (299,792 km/s). The distance between the crests (tops) of two waves is called the wavelength. Electromagnetic wavelengths can vary from a tiny fraction of an inch to more than 50 miles (80 km). Visible light is only a small part of this spectrum, with wavelengths ranging between 380 and 760 millionths of a millimeter.

Humans see different wavelengths in the visible range as different colors. The longest wavelengths appear as red, and the shortest as violet. All the colors of the rainbow fall between these two. The complete mixture of visible wavelengths that comes from the Sun or a light bulb is seen as white light.

Wavelengths slightly longer than visible light are called infrared and are felt as heat. Wavelengths a little shorter than visible light are called ultraviolet (UV). UV radiation provokes the protective darkening of skin exposed to the Sun. Animals other than humans can see some wavelengths of infrared or ultraviolet light.

## Optics

The study of the way light behaves is called optics, from the ancient Greek *optos*, meaning "visible." Light travels in straight lines called rays. When a light ray reaches the surface of an object, it may be absorbed, reflected, or travel through the substance. If all the visible wavelengths of light are absorbed, the object appears black. If some of the wavelengths are absorbed, and others are reflected, the object appears colored. The color people see depends on the mixture of wavelengths reflected. If most light passes through a substance—so that

## HIGHLIGHTS

◆ White light is a mixture of all colors from red to violet. The full color range is called the spectrum.

◆ Light is radiation in waves of electromagnetic energy. However, it often behaves as packets of energy, which have been named photons.

◆ The study of the behavior of light is called optics.

*Light from these electric bulbs floods the surrounding area at 186,282 miles per second (299,792 km/s).*

you can see through it—the substance is called transparent. If the light is scattered as it passes through, the substance is called translucent (tranz-LOO-suhnt) and appears cloudy.

A completely smooth surface acts as a mirror. Each light ray, traveling in a straight line, approaches the mirror at a certain angle, and is reflected at an equal angle. A mirror image of the light source is seen. A rougher surface reflects light at different angles, and no reflection is seen.

### Waves or particles?

One of the first scientists to consider the nature of light was English mathematician and physicist Sir Isaac Newton (1642–1727). Newton believed that light was made up of particles because of the way it travels in straight lines. Dutch physicist and astronomer Christiaan Huygens (1629–1695), however, argued that light travels in waves. Huygens had found that, in certain conditions, one source of light can cancel out another. This is called interference. In the early 1800s, English physicist Thomas Young (1773–1829) and French physicist Augustin Fresnel (1788–1827) conducted experiments demonstrating interference. This seemed to confirm that light travels in waves.

It was not until the early 20th century that it became clear that light somehow behaves both as waves and particles. The tiny light particles are

called photons (FOH-tahnz). A photon has no mass but it has energy. It also has a wavelength, which is a measure of the amount of energy the photon carries. The brightness of a light is due to the number of photons, not to the energy of the individual photons.

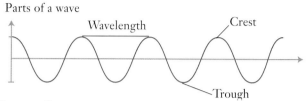

Parts of a wave

### Interference

The interference of light waves is similar to the interference of ripples in a pond. Where two ripples meet, if both are moving up or down at the same moment, their movement is combined to make a bigger ripple. Where one is moving up, and the other down, there is no motion.

Young's experiment involved passing light from a single source through two parallel slits in a screen that blocks light so that they fall on a second screen some distance away. The light passing through each slit behaves like the

*English physicist Thomas Young experimented with light interference and diffraction. He showed that light travels in waves and measured the different wavelengths of visible light.*

source of ripples in a pond. At places on the second screen where the two waves arrive in phase (that is, their crests arrive at the same time), a bright band is formed. Where the waves arrive out of phase, so that the crest of one arrives with the trough of the other, they cancel each other out and no light appears. The difference in phase at any point on the screen is a result of the difference in the distance the light travels to that point from one slit and from the other. The overall result is a series of bright and dark bands called interference fringes.

## Diffraction

A change in the direction of a light wave is called diffraction (di-FRAK-shuhn). If light was made up of particles traveling in straight lines, a shadow would have sharp edges. Instead, shadow edges are blurred as if some light has "leaked" around the object's edge.

The front of each light wave radiates light in all directions, like a ripple in a pond. Waves radiating in any direction other than straight ahead, however, are canceled by waves from other points on the wavefront. When an object is in the way, some of the light travels off at an angle, into the shadow area. Because light from

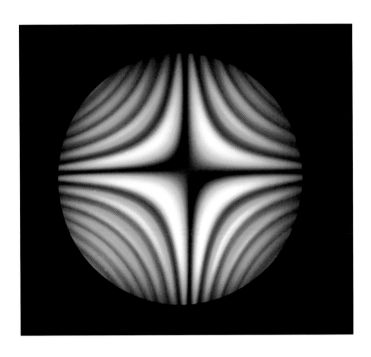

*Light waves can cancel each other out—creating dark bands in interference fringes like these.*

each point close to the edge travels a different distance, interference fringes are formed, making the shadow edge look blurred.

## Refraction

A pencil in a glass of water looks crooked at the point where air and water meet. This is because the light reflected from the part of the pencil that is underwater is bent as it emerges from the water into the air. This is called refraction.

Refraction occurs because light travels more slowly in water, and other transparent substances, than in air. When a ray of light strikes the surface of water or glass at a right angle, it travels straight through. If it strikes at an angle, part of the wavefront slows down, causing the light to turn. The angle through which the light is bent depends on the difference in the speed of light in the two materials.

If a ray of light inside the material meets the surface at a great enough angle, it will be bent back completely and reflected from the surface. This is called total internal reflection. An underwater swimmer sees this effect. The water surface, seen from below, acts like a mirror.

A prism (PRIH-zum) is a piece of glass with faces at different angles. Some prisms use total

---

# EVERYDAY SCIENCE

### The Light Bulb

Most people think Thomas Alva Edison (1847–1931) invented the light bulb. However, much of the work was done earlier. In 1845, another U.S. inventor, J. W. Starr, obtained an English patent for a lamp that used a heated carbon rod in a vacuum. Englishman Joseph Wilson Swan began experimenting around 1860, and Edison started work in 1877. Both succeeded, around 1879, in making a practical lamp using a partially burned thread as the filament inside a vacuum bulb of glass. Edison lost a patent-infringement suit to Swan, and the two eventually went into partnership.

Lamps with carbon filaments were used until 1908, when a process using fine threads of the metal tungsten was discovered. They give out more light and last longer than carbon filaments.

## LOOK CLOSER

# Chemical Reactions

Many chemical reactions are produced by light. These are best explained by regarding light as being made up of the particles called photons (FOH-tahnz).

When a photon strikes an atom, it gives up its energy. This may start a chemical reaction immediately, or it may give the atom enough energy to take part in a later reaction. In photography, the light energy is absorbed by silver compounds in the film. When the film is put into a developer, these compounds release metallic silver, which forms dark areas on the negative, creating the image.

The photon energy can also cause small molecules to join together to form larger molecules called polymers. The energy released when even one photon strikes one molecule can release a fragment of energy that is enough to start a chain reaction. This property is used in some plastics that remain soft until exposed to bright light. Plastics such as these are used in making semiconductor chips.

Ultraviolet (UV) light from the Sun causes several chemical reactions in Earth's air. One of the most important is the production of ozone from oxygen in the upper atmosphere, forming the ozone layer. Ozone helps to filter out UV light and protect living things on Earth. Scientists are now very worried about holes appearing in the ozone layer, caused by humanmade pollutants, that are letting more UV light through.

internal refraction to bend light through right angles, or even through 180 degrees. These prisms are used in periscopes and binoculars.

Different wavelengths of light are refracted through slightly different angles. When a beam of white light is shone through a triangular prism, each wavelength emerges at a slightly different angle. The light is separated into a series of colored bands called a spectrum. A rainbow is formed in a similar way. Sunlight is totally internally reflected inside each tiny raindrop, then refracted into the colors of the spectrum as it emerges.

### The speed of light

Until the 17th century, scientists believed that light traveled instantaneously from place to place. In 1675, Danish astronomer Ole Romer (1644–1710) noticed that the time taken by one of Jupiter's moons to orbit the planet varied. It depended on where Earth was in its orbit. Romer realized that light from Jupiter took longer to reach Earth over a longer distance. From this he calculated the speed of light at 140,000 miles per second (225,000 km/s).

In 1850, French physicist Jean Foucault (1819–1868) flashed a beam of light from a turning mirror to a distant mirror and back. In the time the light took to return, the mirror had turned far enough to deflect the beam a fraction of an inch. From this experiment, Foucault calculated the speed of light with more accuracy. In 1957, the speed of light was defined at 186,282 ± 2 miles per second (299,792 ± 4 km/s).

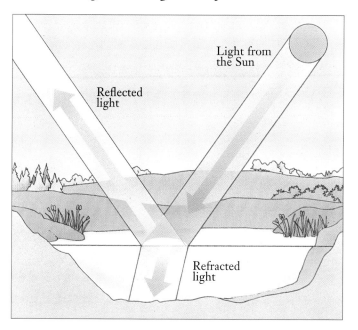

*When sunlight strikes the surface of the water, some of the light is reflected and some is refracted (bent) as it travels through the water.*

### CHECK THESE OUT!

✔COLOR ✔ELECTROMAGNETIC SPECTRUM
✔FIBER OPTICS ✔HOLOGRAPHY ✔OPTICS ✔RAINBOW

# Lightning and Thunder

**The flash of light caused by the flow of electrical charges inside clouds during storms, and the loud accompanying sound**

Lightning is static electricity—the same charge that gives people a shock if they touch a doorknob on a dry winter day, but much more powerful. Lightning and thunder usually occur during storms that develop in hot, humid weather. Warm, moist air rises from Earth to form tall, dark cumulonimbus (KYOO-myuh-luh-NIM-buhs) clouds, also called thunderclouds. These clouds often bring heavy rain. Inside the thundercloud, electrical charges build up. Finally, they surge through the air in a flash of light, accompanied by a loud clap of thunder. Lightning may occur in a single cloud, between clouds, or from a cloud down to the ground.

## Why lightning happens

Electricity is a form of energy caused by a flow of electrons (tiny negatively charged particles). Lightning occurs due to a process called charge separation that happens inside thunderclouds: positive and negative charges that usually exist together are pulled apart. Thunderclouds contain both hailstones and ice crystals. Strong air currents inside the cloud cause the hailstones and ice crystals to collide. This causes friction and a buildup of static electricity. The hailstones become negatively charged and the ice crystals

*Forked lightning flashing from a cloud to the ground during a nighttime thunderstorm.*

## HIGHLIGHTS

◆ Lightning may occur inside a single cloud, between clouds, or from a cloud down to the ground.

◆ There are several different kinds of lightning. They include forked, sheet, and ball lightning.

◆ Thunder is the sound shock wave produced by lightning.

## LOOK CLOSER

## Different Types of Lightning

Forked lightning is made up of many branches. In windy weather, the path of the lightning may be blown sideways, so that each return stroke travels upward in a slightly different place. The resulting flash is called ribbon lightning. Sometimes lightning inside a cloud or traveling between clouds cannot be seen directly, but lights up the sky generally. This is called sheet lightning. Ball lightning is rare and occurs near other lightning. It takes the form of a sphere (ball) of white, yellow, orange, or red light. The size of the lightning ball varies greatly, with balls about 8 inches (20 cm) across being the most common.

become positively charged. Powerful vertical air currents carry the negative charge to the bottom of the cloud. The top part of the cloud becomes positively charged. Eventually, when the charges in the two areas build up enough, a pulse of electricity flows to balance them out.

Clouds are not the only places where electrical charges build up. The strong negative charge at the base of the cloud causes the air near the ground below the cloud to develop a positive charge. Eventually, when the imbalance between charges becomes strong enough, a spark of electricity leaps between the two, and that is lightning. The lightning takes the quickest route to the ground, often running down tall objects such as trees. For this reason, it is dangerous to take shelter under trees during a thunderstorm.

### Lightning strikes

A stroke of lightning develops in several stages. When the negative charge at the bottom of the cloud becomes powerful enough, a stream of electrons flows down toward Earth in short, jagged bursts. As the bolt of lightning approaches the ground, a positive charge called a streamer moves up into the air through a tall object such as a tree. When the downward-moving lightning meets the

*A negative (−) charge in a cloud induces a positive (+) charge in the ground. A flash of lightning evens this out.*

streamer, electrons flow into the ground. A strong, bright pulse of electricity called a return stroke carries a positive charge up into the cloud. The first return stroke is often followed by a series of other pulses, but this happens so quickly that all that is seen is a single flash.

### Thunder

Lightning often generates a clap of thunder, which is a type of sound shock wave. During the return stroke, the strong pulse traveling upward heats the surrounding air. The sudden heating causes the air to expand and explode.

Because light travels at great speed, lightning is seen almost the instant it is produced. Sound travels much more slowly, and the farther away the lightning strikes, the longer the sound waves take to arrive. People use this to work out how far away they are from a lightning strike. It takes five seconds for sound to travel about a mile.

***CHECK THESE OUT!***
✔ATMOSPHERE ✔CLOUD ✔ELECTRICITY

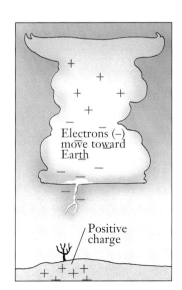

Electrons (−) move toward Earth

Positive charge

A streamer (+) moves up through a tall object

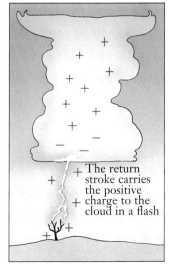

The return stroke carries the positive charge to the cloud in a flash

# Limestone

**A sedimentary rock composed mainly of calcium carbonate**

A rock is called limestone when more than half of it is calcium carbonate, usually in the crystalline form called calcite (KAL-SYT). Limestones usually also contain plenty of sand grains and clay. Limestones are pale sedimentary (SEH-duh-MEN-tuh-ree) rocks, being gray, yellowish, brown, or even white. Sometimes impurities make limestones dark—even black.

Many limestones differ from other sedimentary rocks in that important chemical (as opposed to physical) processes affect their formation. The calcite in limestone can be formed by precipitation (separation) from seawater or it can come from the fossilized remains of creatures such as corals, crinoids (related to starfish), or mollusks. All these creatures make calcite shells or skeletons. When they die, their soft parts decay or are eaten, but the shells remain. These are often broken up by erosion and may form a fine calcite mud on the seabed. Within the mud, there may be the fossils of mollusk shells and other whole organisms that have been rapidly buried in the lime mud before they could be broken up. Limestone forms when

*A Karst landscape showing a limestone pavement that has been weathered by acidic rainwater.*

## HIGHLIGHTS

◆ Limestone forms when layers of sediment containing much calcium carbonate plus some sand and clay are deposited on the seabed.

◆ Many limestones are made up of the remains of dead organisms.

◆ Limestone is a valuable resource, used in road making, agriculture, and industry.

the mud hardens as the calcite crystallizes. Limestones that have many broken or whole fossils are called shelly or skeletal limestones.

## Types of limestone

Limestones are named after the main types of fossils they contain; for example, crinoidal limestone is full of crinoids. Chalk, a very fine-grained pure limestone, is made almost entirely of the tiny skeletons of algae. Oolitic (OH-uh-LIH-tik) limestone is made of small, rounded grains called ooliths, 1 mm in diameter. Ooliths (OH-uh-LYTHZ) form in warm, shallow seawater

## LOOK CLOSER

Limestones are found in all the geological periods, and many are forming today. Most are formed in the sea and contain excellent fossils of long-extinct creatures. These help geologists (scientists who study rocks) to understand how life has changed over time. The shallow seas in which many limestones were formed were rich in mollusks, corals, crinoids, and brachiopods (soft animals with two shells). Some limestones are ancient coral reefs, buried under limy mud, containing the remains of all the creatures that lived along with the coral on the reef. Such deposits allow geologists to study the natural history of a coral reef of the past.

## Limestone and Fossils

*Nummulitic limestone, so called because it contains marine organisms called nummulites.*

that is constantly moved about by waves and tides. A sand grain or fossil fragment is in the center of an oolith. As the warm water moves, layers of lime are deposited around the particle, like the skins of an onion. This process happens today on the Grand Bahama Banks, off the coast of Florida. Many ancient limestones, hundreds of millions of years old, are oolitic.

Micrite (MY-kryt) is the name given to limestone with very small grains (less than 0.04 mm across). Micrite is formed from lime-rich mud that accumulated on a quiet seabed, or possibly in a lagoon, cut off from rough seas.

Some limestones do not contain fossils. Travertine (TRA-vuhr-TEEN) is a limestone created when lime-rich water evaporates in rivers, springs, lakes, and caves. It can also occur around hot springs where the water flows away.

Dolomite (DOH-luh-MYT) is a carbonate of calcium and magnesium found in many limestones. When it forms a high proportion of a rock, the rock is called dolomite or dolostone. Dolostone probably forms when limestones are chemically altered after their formation, perhaps as a result of a reaction between a layer of limestone on the seabed and seawater.

### Limestone in the landscape

Groundwater and rainwater are commonly acidic. Calcium carbonate reacts with both to form a bicarbonate of calcium that is soluble and is washed away. Limestone is thus removed by chemical weathering. This process enlarges the joints (vertical lines) and bedding planes (horizontal layers) in the rock, and underground cave systems are created. Karst landscapes are formed by this process. Such landscapes have very little surface water, as it tends to flow away through the cracks in the rock. There is much bare limestone on the surface, as plants can grow only when there is water present. Below ground there may be great cave systems filled with stalactites and stalagmites. In some cases, the cave roof may collapse to make a deep gorge.

### Uses of limestone

Limestone and related rocks are used for building and as decorative rocks. A great deal of limestone is crushed for use in road building. Limestone is also used in the steel, glass, and ceramic industries. If limestone is heated, it leaves calcium oxide (quicklime). This is used extensively in agriculture to improve acid soils and to make cement, plaster, and mortar.

Underground limestones can be important water, gas, and oil reservoirs, as the rock is porous (fluids can be held in them or travel through them). Many limestone layers contain valuable reserves of lead, zinc, and fluorite.

### CHECK THESE OUT!
✔CAVE ✔LANDFORM ✔ROCK ✔SEDIMENTARY ROCK

# Lipid

## Fatty substance
## found in all living organisms

Lipids are compounds found in living cells. They include natural fatty substances such as fats, oils, and waxes. Lipids do not dissolve in water but can be extracted from cells using organic solvents such as alcohols, ethers, and chloroform. The structure of most lipids contains a compound called an ester. Esters are formed by the reaction of an acid and an alcohol.

### Fats and oils

Fats and oils are esters formed from a reaction between glycerol (GLIH-suh-ROHL; an alcohol) and long-chain fatty acids ($C_xH_yCOOH$). Fats and oils are also called triglycerides because each glycerol unit links to three acid groups. Fats are triglycerides that are solids at room temperature, and oils are liquids at room temperature.

Vegetable oils are obtained by crushing the seeds or fruit of a plant. Olive, corn, sunflower, and linseed oils are extracted in this way. Animal fats are collected by boiling fatty animal parts in water. The fat melts and floats on top of the water and so can be skimmed off.

### Saturated and unsaturated fats

Fats and oils are classed as saturated or unsaturated, depending on the makeup of their fatty acids. Saturated fatty acids contain the

## HIGHLIGHTS

♦ Fats and oils are compounds of glycerol with long-chain organic acids called fatty acids.

♦ Boiling fats with a sodium hydroxide solution produces soap.

♦ Phospholipids form the cell walls of living organisms.

*Coconut oil is a lipid extracted from coconut flesh. It is a saturated oil that can be used to make soap.*

maximum number of hydrogen atoms for each carbon atom, and these are linked together with single bonds. Polyunsaturated fatty acids have two or more double bonds in their chains and fewer hydrogen atoms. A monounsaturated fatty acid has one double bond in its chain. Double bonds reduce the melting point of a triglyceride, so oils tend to be less saturated than fats. A process called hydrogenation changes unsaturated fats into saturated fats by adding hydrogen to the double bonds. This process is used to change unsaturated oils into spreadable fats (margarines).

The double bonds in unsaturated fats and oils can react with oxygen in air and with reactive chemicals called free radicals. In the body, unsaturated fats are thought to soak up free radicals and prevent them from causing cell damage. When linseed oil reacts with oxygen, links form between the double bonds in neighboring molecules. These links change the

**Making Paints From Natural Oils**

Gloss paints have an oily odor that gives a clue to their origin. Typical gloss paint contains alkyd (AL-kuhd) resins, which are made by processing natural oils. Heating an oil with glycerol causes the fatty acid groups in the oil to move between molecules. This will eventually produce a mixture that contains mainly monoglycerides (glycerol molecules attached to only one fatty acid group). Adding a compound that has two acid groups, such as phthalic (THA-lik) acid, causes the monoglycerides to form polyester chains. In these chains, a fatty acid group hangs from each glycerol unit. This produces alkyd resin, which is then thinned with a solvent before being mixed with color pigments and additives to make paint. These additives make the paint apply well and dry quickly. Spreading the paint over a surface helps the solvent to evaporate. Oxygen in the air then forms links between unsaturated fatty acid groups in the alkyd, hardening the film. The combination of oils in the resin influences how quickly the paint hardens and how well it keeps its color with time. In this way, alkyd resins can be used to make a variety of paints and protective coatings.

runny oil into a hard film. This is why linseed oil is used to make varnishes, which harden when they are exposed to the air.

## Making soaps from oils and fats

Oils and fats can be split into glycerol and fatty acids by boiling them with sodium hydroxide solution. Adding sodium chloride solution causes salts in the fatty acids to solidify. This solid is washed and dried to make soap. Animal fats make standard soaps, while palm and olive oils make high-quality soaps. Perfume can be added to soap to mask the smell of the fatty acid salt. Soaps remove grease because they have a hydrocarbon chain that attracts fat and a neutralized acid group that attracts water. Soap particles surround grease and dig their hydrocarbon "tails" into it. Water attracts the neutralized acid groups and washes away the grease.

## Waxes

Most waxes are esters of long-chain fatty acids with alcohols. They have a single alcohol group attached to a hydrocarbon chain that has 16 to 36 carbon atoms. A typical wax is cetyl palmitate, which is found in sperm whale oil. The wax of the carnauba (kahr-NAW-buh) palm is used to give a hard, glossy finish to candles and to polish floors. Earwax and beeswax are other waxes.

## Phospholipids

Phospholipids (FAHS-FOH-LIH-puhdz) are important components in the walls of living cells. Like fats and oils, they are based on glycerol. However, their esters contain a phosphate group as well as fatty acid chains. Phospholipids arrange themselves in double layers to form watertight cell walls. The hydrocarbon portions of these two layers tangle together, while the water-loving phosphate groups form the inner and outer surfaces of the cell walls.

***CHECK THESE OUT!***
✔DETERGENT ✔ORGANIC CHEMISTRY

# Liquid

Solids, liquids, and gases all consist of particles that may be atoms, molecules, or ions. Most liquids and gases consist of molecules; some consist of atoms. The particles of a solid are packed closely together, so solids are difficult to compress. Particles in a gas are widely spaced and move so rapidly that a gas will completely fill the space available to it.

Particles in liquids are almost as tightly packed as particles in solids, so liquids are difficult to compress. Particles in liquids can slip past one another, so liquids have no fixed shape. They are denser than gases, so gravity holds a liquid in the bottom of its container.

### Attractive forces in liquids

Three types of force hold molecules together in liquids: polar forces, hydrogen bonding, and London dispersion forces. Molecules are held together by polar force if electrons are not spread evenly through the molecules. In a molecule such as trichloromethane ($CHCl_3$),

*When a water droplet falls on a pool of water, it forms a crater. The pool surface then collapses, and the water forms a column.*

## HIGHLIGHTS

◆ The atoms or molecules in liquids are closely packed but are free to move around each other.

◆ Liquids mix well together if they have similar molecular structures.

chlorine nuclei pull electrons toward them more strongly than the molecule's other nuclei. As a result, each chlorine atom has a slight negative charge, while the rest of the molecule has a slight positive charge. This type of molecule is called polar because the imbalance of electrons creates poles of positive and negative electrical charge. Opposite charges attract, so molecules in liquid trichloromethane align themselves so that either the positive pole of each molecule is close to the negative poles of its neighbors, or the other way around. This causes an electrostatic attraction that does not occur between nonpolar molecules.

Hydrogen bonding happens between molecules with a hydrogen atom attached to a highly electronegative atom, such as oxygen or fluorine, which pulls on the shared electrons. This leaves the hydrogen atom with a slight positive charge, which attracts other molecules. Atoms of elements such as oxygen, nitrogen, and fluorine also have at least one lone pair (electrons that do not take part in bonding). The positively charged hydrogen atom of one molecule is strongly attracted to a lone pair of another molecule, forming a hydrogen bond. Ethanol ($C_2H_5OH$) forms hydrogen bonds between the hydrogen atom of the alcohol group (-OH) of one molecule and the oxygen atom of another.

London dispersion forces are the only attraction between nonpolar molecules unable to form hydrogen bonds. Tetrachloromethane ($CCl_4$) is an example of such a molecule. German-born U.S. physicist Fritz London (1900–1954) first explained these forces in 1930. The cloud of electrons in any particular molecule is constantly wobbling around the framework of nuclei. This movement causes regions of positive and negative charge in that molecule. As this happens, the temporary positive charge attracts the electron clouds of neighboring molecules, while the temporary negative charge repels their electrons. London forces act between polar molecules but are weaker than polar attraction.

## Mixtures and solutions

Liquids that mix have similar balances of polar attractions, hydrogen bonding, and London forces between their molecules. This is called "like mixing with like," since liquids that mix well

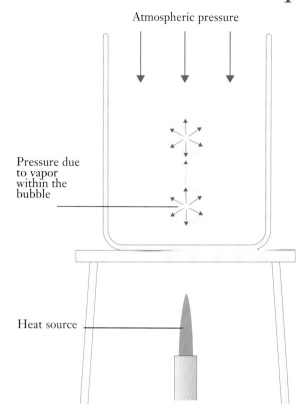

Atmospheric pressure

Pressure due to vapor within the bubble

Heat source

*When a liquid boils, the pressure of the vapor within a bubble pushes the liquid aside against the opposing atmospheric pressure.*

often have similar chemical structures. Propanol ($C_3H_7OH$) mixes perfectly with ethanol because the molecules of both have alcohol groups (-OH) that are polar and can form hydrogen bonds. Liquids that do not mix have different balances of attractive forces. Hexane ($C_6H_{14}$) will not mix with water ($H_2O$) because it cannot form polar attractions or hydrogen bonds with water. Instead, the two liquids form separate layers. Hexane, which is less dense than water, floats on the water layer. In their separate layer, water molecules are surrounded by other water molecules, which attract them far more strongly than do hexane molecules.

Liquids and solids form mixtures called solutions. Nonpolar liquids dissolve nonpolar solids, so hexane will dissolve nonpolar waxes, for example. Water is the best solvent for most salts, since its polarity attracts the charged ions in salts.

### CHECK THESE OUT!

✔CAPILLARY ACTION ✔DIFFUSION ✔FORCE
✔GAS ✔MATTER ✔OSMOSIS ✔SOLID ✔WATER

---

# STORY OF SCIENCE

## Brownian Motion

British botanist Robert Brown (1773–1858) made an important discovery in 1827 at the British Museum in London, England. While studying a suspension of pollen grains in water through a microscope, he noticed that the grains were moving around in a jittery way. He first thought this was a sign of some life force in the pollen but soon discovered particles from mineral sources behaved in the same way.

The motion happened because water molecules were constantly bombarding the pollen particles. These molecules hit the pollen randomly from all angles, which is why the motion of the pollen particles was so erratic. Water molecules cannot be seen through the microscope, since they are much smaller than the pollen particles. Even so, they move so quickly that they have enough momentum to knock around the relatively massive pollen particles.

German-born U.S. physicist Albert Einstein (1879–1955) calculated the mechanics of these collisions in 1905. He included the result in his kinetic theory, which is a mathematical description of how particles move in substances.

# Liquid Crystal

**A substance that exists in a state halfway between a solid crystal and a liquid**

Most crystals melt (turn from a solid state into a liquid state) when they are heated. Some, however, go through a mesomorphic (MES-oh-MAWR-fik) state. They have some of the properties of the solid crystal and some of a liquid and so are called liquid crystals. Many are in this state at normal temperatures. Natural liquid crystals are common in biological systems. They are vital in the membranes that enclose cells in the human body. Synthetic liquid crystals are essential in digital watches, calculators, and laptop computer screens.

*Liquid crystal displays are found in the screens of portable computers, such as the one below.*

The first scientific study of liquid crystals was carried out in 1888 by German physicist Otto Lehmann (1855–1922). Working with the compound cholesteryl benzoate, Lehmann observed that it appeared to have two separate melting points. It melted into a cloudy liquid at 294°F (145.5°C). Then, at 353.3°F (178.5°C), its appearance changed from cloudy to clear. Mixtures of substances will behave in this way, but most pure crystals have a single sharp melting point.

All crystals have a very distinct structure. Atoms or molecules are held at fixed points in a lattice by the forces between them. The molecules of a liquid crystal are rod-shaped and are lined up in a specific direction. Heating the crystal gives the molecules enough energy to move out of their fixed positions and so the crystals melt. However, they still do not have enough energy to move out of alignment. It is only when they are heated

# EVERYDAY SCIENCE

### Liquid Crystal Displays

Liquid crystal displays (LCDs) are used in calculators, cellular phones, and portable computer screens. The image is made up of thousands of tiny LCDs called pixels (short for "picture elements"). In calculators and watches, any digit from 0 to 9 can be made up simply from seven dash-shaped pixels.

The first LCD was made in 1963 at the Radio Corporation of America. It used a liquid crystal material that becomes opaque (blocks light) in an electric field. The material was sandwiched between two transparent sheets acting as electrodes. When the sheets received an electric current, the crystal material became opaque.

This early type of LCD was soon replaced by an improved version, the so-called twisted nematic display, which is clearer to read. Again the liquid crystal is sandwiched between two transparent electrodes, but in this case the electrodes are between sheets of film that polarize (channel) the light. Tiny grooves on the inside of each electrode surface cause the direction of all the liquid crystal molecules in between to twist by 90 degrees. In this position, the crystals allow light to pass from one side to the other. When an electric current is applied between the electrodes, however, the liquid crystals untwist and light can no longer pass through. The pixels look dark against a lighter background.

The supertwist nematic LCD twists the liquid crystal through 270 degrees. Supertwists produce a higher contrast between the dark and light parts of displays, making them even easier to read.

to a higher temperature that the crystal structure is broken up. The direction along which the molecules are aligned is called the director.

The structure of many crystals causes them to polarize light—that is, the light they let through vibrates in only one direction. It was the discovery that liquid crystals had polarizing properties that proved they still kept their molecular alignment.

## Types of liquid crystals

Researchers have divided liquid crystals into three major types. In nematic (nee-MAT-ik) crystals, the molecules in the liquid are all in alignment, but they are at many scattered levels. A smectic crystal, however, is made up of distinct layers of molecules. The molecules in one layer are lined up in one direction, but the molecules in the next layer may point in a different direction. The third type is called cholesteric or chiral (KY-ruhl). The name *chiral* comes from the Greek and means "handedness." It can refer to either left- or right-handedness. In these liquid crystals, the direction of the molecules is not constant, as in nematic crystals. It gradually changes at different depths in the crystal. This forms a twist that can be either left-handed or right-handed. The degree of twist changes with temperature and also affects the color of light reflected from the crystals. Some scientists believe DNA may be a cholesteric liquid crystal.

## Physical properties

As well as the way in which light is transmitted, the structure of liquid crystals gives them other special properties. One is very important in the design and manufacture of liquid crystal displays (LCDs). If each molecule has a small negative charge at one end and a small positive charge at the other, it will change direction to line up in an electric field. So for the crystal as a whole, the director will align with the direction of the electric field. Other liquid crystals can be affected by a magnetic field in a similar way. Some will align with the magnetic field, while others will turn at right angles to it.

***CHECK THESE OUT!***
✔CRYSTAL ✔LIQUID

# Luminescence

**Light emission from a material after it has absorbed radiant or chemical energy**

Some substances seem to shine brightly even when there is little or no light falling on them. For example, the hands of an alarm clock glow in the dark and a cyclist's safety gear shows up vividly in a car's headlights. This property is called luminescence (LOO-muh-NEH-suhnts).

Every atom has a nucleus (center) surrounded by electrons occupying different energy levels. When electromagnetic radiation—which can be light, infrared heat, ultraviolet rays, or X rays—strikes an atom, it may be absorbed. All electromagnetic radiation consists of packets of energy called photons (FOH-tahnz).

The energy of the radiation causes an electron to be raised to a higher energy level. This can be compared to taking a ball up a flight of stairs. At the top of the stairs, the ball has potential energy, which it can spend by bouncing down the stairs. In the same way, an electron can return to a lower energy level. When it does so, it gives out the excess energy as a photon of light.

There are two kinds of luminescence. Each depends on the length of time that lapses before electrons return to their low energy level. When the electrons return immediately, the light that is given out is called fluorescence (floo-REH-suhnts). If the energizing radiation stops, the fluorescence stops. Some materials, on the other hand, will continue to glow, sometimes for days, even when there is no further radiation. This is called phosphorescence (FAHS-fuh-REH-suhnts).

Thermoluminescent minerals begin to phosphoresce when heated to a relatively low

*Crayons containing luminescent dyes fluoresce (glow) a variety of different colors under ultraviolet light.*

## HIGHLIGHTS

♦ Luminescent materials absorb energy and then release it as light.

♦ Luminescence is called fluorescence if it ceases as soon as the source of energy stops. It is called phosphorescence if it continues after the light source is removed.

♦ Luminescence can be triggered by different energy sources. For example, thermoluminescence is produced by low heat.

♦ Many living species use oxygen in chemical reactions to produce luminescence.

♦ Luminescent materials are used in television and computer screens and fluorescent (neon) lighting.

# EVERYDAY SCIENCE

## Thermoluminescent Minerals

In the 17th century, scientists discovered thermoluminescence in minerals. They found that barite (barium sulfate) would phosphoresce in sunlight after it had been heated and cooled. Some 3,000 different minerals behave in this way. The heat raises electrons to a high energy level, but when the mineral cools, they drop to a middle level called an electron trap. The sunlight, or some other energy source, raises them out of the trap, and they fall to their low energy level, releasing photons.

Geologists (scientists who study the structure and history of rocks) and archaeologists (people who study past human life as revealed by ancient relics) date and analyze materials by measuring the strength of their thermoluminescence. Measuring thermoluminescence in meteorites and Moon rocks that land on Earth can give an idea of where they originated in the Solar System.

temperature. Fluorite (calcium fluoride) is one of these minerals. This is not the same as materials glowing when they are heated strongly (incandescence). Energy sources other than light and low heat can cause materials to luminesce. For example, high-frequency sound waves can prompt a sudden release of intense light. Chemical reactions may also produce luminescence. This usually occurs in the presence of oxygen. The yellow form of the element phosphorus glows with a green light as it reacts with the oxygen in the air. Luminol is a synthetic compound that emits a bright blue light when it is oxidized. It is used in forensic science to detect traces of blood.

Many living organisms use oxygen in chemical reactions to produce luminescence. Fireflies use their light as a mating signal. Their larvae (young, wingless insects), which are called glowworms, also have a bright yellowish glow. When ocean water is churned up, more oxygen becomes dissolved in it. Tiny creatures in the water called protozoans (PROH-tuh-ZOH-uhnz) produce a soft, yellow-green shimmer. Other species of land and marine animals are also luminescent. They include some bacteria, fungi, snails, octopuses, squids, worms, shrimps, beetles, and fish.

## Human uses for luminescence

Fluorescent lamps are good examples of luminescence produced by electricity. The glass tubes are filled with gases such as neon or nitrogen or the vapor of a metal such as mercury. Electrodes inside the tube are connected to the power supply, and the electric field between the electrodes raises the energy levels of the gas atoms. They either fluoresce directly or transfer their energy to a coating inside the tube. This coating is made up of phosphorescent materials called phosphors.

Phosphors are also used in television, computer, and radar screens. Electrons are emitted from a heated cathode at the back end of the tube, focused by a magnetic field, and then they bombard the phosphors on the coated front of the tube. Different phosphors give out different colors of light.

Luminescent compounds are added to fabrics to mask the yellowish white of natural fibers. These absorb ultraviolet light and give out blue light, making the fibers appear whiter. White fabric treated with these brighteners glows blue-lilac under pure ultraviolet light. Similar compounds are added to inks, paints, and crayons to brighten their colors.

### CHECK THESE OUT!
✔ATOM ✔ELECTRON ✔ENERGY ✔LIGHT
✔QUANTUM THEORY

# Lunar Mission

## Spacecraft sent to explore the Moon

The Moon is Earth's closest companion in space but is still about 250,000 miles (400,000 km) away. From the earliest days of the Space Age, when the first satellites were launched in 1957, the Moon was an obvious target for space missions. Getting a spacecraft farther than a low Earth orbit (a few hundred miles above Earth) was a huge engineering task. The early lunar probes also tested many of the systems that are now used to navigate to, and send data back from, the farthest reaches of the Solar System.

### Early Soviet missions

In the late 1950s and 1960s, the Soviet Union took the lead in the space race with the first satellite launch and the first astronaut in orbit. Mostly this was because they had more powerful rockets than the U.S. National Aeronautics and Space Administration (NASA). The Soviet rockets also allowed them to take the lead in the race to the Moon. The first lunar mission, *Luna 1*, was launched on January 2, 1959, and aimed simply to hit the Moon. It ended up missing its target by over 3,000 miles (5,000 km), but this was amazingly accurate considering it was the first spacecraft ever to leave Earth's orbit.

Later that year, the Soviets had more success. *Luna 2* hit the Moon on September 13. On October 4, 1959, *Luna 3* looped around the Moon, photographing the far side, which is permanently turned away from Earth. Nine grainy photographs of this region were developed automatically on board the space probe, then scanned and sent back to Earth as a radio signal when *Luna 3* reappeared from behind the Moon. Interestingly, the far side of the Moon is quite different from the near side. There are none of the low plains (maria) that are the most striking features when the Moon is observed from Earth.

As the Luna missions developed, navigation became more accurate, and probes carried a wider variety of instruments in order to send back information about magnetism and radiation. The early lunar probes were the first spacecraft to fly outside Earth's protective magnetic field. At the time, no one knew quite what interplanetary space would be like.

### Soft landings

The next challenge was to make a soft landing on the Moon. This required a new series of more complex probes, but the Soviets now began to hit a run of bad luck. *Luna 4*'s rocket failed, sending it crashing back into the Pacific Ocean in 1963. In 1965, three other Luna probes crashed into the Moon at full speed, while another missed the Moon completely.

On January 31, 1966, the Soviets' run of bad luck ended with *Luna 9*. This probe had two parts—a mother ship that contained rockets to slow its descent to the Moon, and a 220-pound (100-kg) spherical landing capsule that was dropped from the mother ship before it crashed onto the surface. The capsule survived a rough landing and then unfolded its aerials to beam back pictures

# HIGHLIGHTS

◆ In the 1950s and 1960s, the Moon was the most important goal for both U.S. and Soviet space programs.

◆ The U.S.S.R. had a series of successes with its Luna probes. The probes made the first crash and soft landings.

from the surface of the Moon. *Luna 9* was a landmark mission because it proved for the first time the Moon had a solid, rocky surface. Scientists had worried that the surface could have become so powdery, from meteors smashing into it from space, that any spacecraft landing there would sink into the surface and be lost.

*Lunas 10* through *14* were a new generation of orbiting spacecraft. They were the first to go into orbit around an object other than Earth. Each carried cameras that could take far more detailed pictures of Earth's surface than anything before.

## The United States catches up

During the gap between the early Luna missions and the later Soviet successes, the United States's NASA had begun to develop its own series of

*A lunar module pilot walks away from the Lunar Roving Vehicle during an extravehicular activity.*

Moon probes. Unlike the Lunas, which steadily evolved from mission to mission, NASA planned three separate types of probe. They were committed to putting a U.S. astronaut on the Moon by the end of the 1960s.

The three U.S. probe series were the Rangers, the Lunar Orbiters, and the Surveyors. The Rangers were developed first. They were designed to crash into the Moon, radioing pictures back to Earth right up to the moment when the probe was destroyed. The first two Rangers were tests, and the first three lunar missions, *Rangers 3* through *5*, suffered various failures trying to reach the Moon. *Ranger 6* made it to the Moon, but its camera failed during its descent, and no pictures were returned. NASA finally succeeded with *Ranger 7*, which crashed onto the Moon on July 31, 1964, returning thousands of pictures. *Rangers 8* and *9* followed

in 1965 and were also successful. The Rangers returned 17,255 images of the lunar surface, showing details down to 10 inches (25 cm) across—1,000 times smaller than anything visible from Earth.

NASA had more luck with its Lunar Orbiter probes, launched between August 1966 and August 1967. These five spacecraft entered orbits that flew over all but one percent of the Moon's surface and sent back a detailed photographic survey that NASA used to select potential landing sites for a crewed mission.

The third prong of NASA's attack on the Moon, the Surveyor program, ran at the same time as the Lunar Orbiters. The Surveyors were designed to follow up Ranger with a series of soft landings to gain more information about the state of the lunar surface. *Surveyor 1* landed successfully on May 30, 1966, on a volcanic plain called the Ocean of Storms. The probe confirmed that the lunar surface was stable, and it sent back thousands of television pictures to Earth. *Surveyor 2* failed when its rocket thrusters sent it spinning out of control, but *Surveyor 3* landed successfully on April 17, 1967. This probe was more advanced, carrying a robot scoop that dug trenches in the lunar surface and tested their strength. This added to information about how stable the material was and what sort of weights the Moon's surface could support.

Although *Surveyor 4* crashed into the Moon after losing contact with Earth during its descent, the final three Surveyors were great successes. By the start of 1968, NASA felt it knew enough about the Moon to successfully put a crewed vehicle on its surface.

## Preparing for Apollo

Planning for the crewed Apollo program had already been under way for many years— ever since 1961, when President John F. Kennedy had set the goal of a landing by 1970. The project was one of the most ambitious engineering feats ever undertaken. It involved building the

largest rocket ever built (*Saturn V*) and a complex three-part spacecraft that would have to separate and recombine in orbit around the Moon. NASA had been practicing many of the techniques the mission would need in the Gemini program, so it was ready to go.

The first Apollo missions were uncrewed tests. *Apollo 4* simply test-fired the *Saturn V* rocket, and *Apollo 5* tested the Apollo spacecraft in Earth's orbit. The first crewed mission, *Apollo 7*, was also confined to Earth's orbit.

Meanwhile, the Soviet Union had been planning its own mission to the Moon. As the Luna missions continued to look for possible landing sites, a series of Zond missions sent dummy spacecraft, sometimes with animals on board, to the Moon. The Soviet plan seems to have been to put a rocket in Earth's orbit and then,

*Astronaut Edwin "Buzz" Aldrin climbs down from the Lunar Module as he prepares to walk on the Moon.*

in a separate launch, send a crew to meet it. However, problems with their rockets caused delays, and by the time the program was ready to start again, the Americans were on the Moon.

## Apollo and after

Following three more test flights that put astronauts into orbit around the Moon for the first time, *Apollo 11* finally touched down on July 20, 1969, in the lunar Sea of Tranquillity. Neil Armstrong became the first person to walk on the Moon. The Apollo program was a huge success. Five more missions landed in various parts of the Moon between 1969 and 1972, collecting rock samples, setting up instruments, and even driving a car—the Lunar Roving Vehicle—on the Moon. *Apollo 12* actually set down within walking distance of *Surveyor 3* and collected parts of the earlier probe to see how they had lasted on the Moon.

Although they abandoned their plans to send cosmonauts to the Moon after the Americans got there first, the Soviet space agency continued to explore the Moon with a new generation of Luna probes. *Lunas 16, 20,* and *24* were fitted with robot arms to collect lunar soil, deposit it into a recovery capsule, and then send the capsule back to Earth. *Lunas 17* and *21* each carried a remote-controlled robot rover called *Lunokhod*, fitted with solar panels that allowed it to drive around on the lunar surface for months, returning thousands of pictures. The lander missions *Lunas 18* and *23* were failures. *Lunas 19, 21,* and *22* were orbiter missions. When *Luna 24* blasted its samples back to Earth in 1976, it was the last mission targeted at the Moon for 13 years.

## Return to the Moon

The 1990s saw a revival of interest in the Moon. On January 24, 1990, Japan launched a probe called *Hiten*, designed mainly to test systems for interplanetary probes, into an orbit that carried it past the Moon several times. On the first pass, it released a daughter probe called *Hagomoro* into lunar orbit. A failed transmitter meant *Hagomoro* was unable to send back any data.

In February 1994, the U.S. satellite *Clementine* arrived in Earth's orbit. This probe was designed as a military test satellite and was equipped with

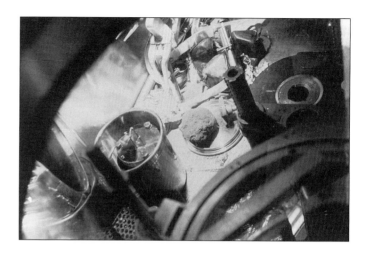

*Moon rock collected from the* **Apollo 11** *mission is examined in a laboratory on Earth.*

a variety of sensors to detect missile launches. Once its main mission was over, it was diverted into orbit around the Moon. *Clementine* used its cameras to produce the first color maps of the lunar surface and to search for ice in the deep, permanently shadowed craters at the Moon's poles. The probe found that the bottoms of some of these craters were highly reflective. It was not equipped to prove the existence of ice, however.

In 1998, NASA followed up *Clementine* with the purpose-built *Lunar Prospector*. This probe used remote-sensing technology developed for finding minerals on Earth to survey the Moon and build up maps of metal and mineral deposits.

*Lunar Surveyor* also looked for ice at the Moon's south pole—astronomers think water could have been dumped there by collisions with comets during the formation of the Solar System. If this is correct, it could be a boost for future colonization of the Moon. This time, the evidence was convincing but still not conclusive.

On September 3, 1999, at the end of its mission, *Lunar Prospector* smashed into a crater where scientists thought water might lurk. Astronomers studying the impact from Earth hoped it might throw up a cloud of ice that they could detect, but they found nothing. So the mystery is still unsolved—it will have to wait for a future mission to the Moon.

***CHECK THESE OUT!***
✔APOLLO MISSION ✔MOON ✔SPACE

# Magellan

**Robotic space probe that mapped the surface of Venus using radar**

The *Magellan* (muh-JEL-uhn) spacecraft was launched in 1989. It spent three years in orbit around the planet Venus, mapping the surface with an advanced form of radar. Venus's atmosphere is thick, cloudy, and corrosive (eats away at materials), so cameras cannot peer down to the surface. Probes that land on the planet are broken down within a few minutes. Before *Magellan*, other spacecraft had carried radar to Venus, but *Magellan* was able to see details 300 feet (100 m) across and to build three-dimensional maps of the surface.

## Early missions to Venus

The first spacecraft to visit Venus had been the Mariner probes of the early 1960s. These spacecraft had flown past the planet but did not go into orbit around it or attempt to land. They revealed that Venus had a surface temperature of around 800°F (425°C) and a thick acidic atmosphere with a pressure 100 times greater than the air pressure on Earth.

The first attempt to land on Venus was made by Soviet probe *Venera 4* in 1967. The probe descended on parachutes, sending back information for 94 minutes before losing contact as it approached the ground. In 1970, *Venera 7* made it to the surface and sent back information for 23 minutes, while in 1975, *Venera 9* sent back the first pictures from the surface.

The only way to understand what Venus is like was to peer through the clouds. The best way to do this was using radar—bouncing a radio signal down to the surface and detecting the echo. Radio waves would pass through clouds without

interference, and the length of time the signals took to return would show the distance to the surface, indicating highland and lowland areas.

The first spacecraft to carry radar to Venus was the U.S. National Aeronautics and Space Administration's (NASA's) *Pioneer Venus Orbiter*, launched in 1978. This was followed by two Soviet probes, *Venera 15* and *16*. *Pioneer Venus Orbiter* could only map the surface down to details 60 miles across. *Venera 15* and *16* built up much more accurate maps of small areas of the planet, showing features only 1¼ miles (2 km) across. These early probes showed that Venus had three major areas of raised highlands, valleys, mountain ranges, and impact craters.

## The Magellan mission

*Magellan* evolved from plans for an ambitious mission called the Venus Orbiting Imaging Radar (VOIR). This probe would have carried six instruments to study Venus's atmosphere, alongside an advanced synthetic aperture radar (SAR) to study the surface. However, NASA decided VOIR was too expensive and scrapped it. Some of the project's scientists proposed a smaller probe to carry just the SAR to Venus. This was eventually given the go-ahead in 1984. The spacecraft was named for Portugese explorer Ferdinand Magellan (lived c. 1480–1521).

The probe was 20 feet (6 m) long, 15 feet (4.5 m) across, and weighed more than 3 tons (2.7 tonnes). The spacecraft was fitted with solar panels to provide it with electricity and an elaborate guidance system to keep it correctly positioned. The SAR radar worked by sending out two radar beams and combining the information from them. A small, horn-shaped antenna bounced radar signals off the ground directly below the spacecraft, while a much larger

## HIGHLIGHTS

♦ The Magellan probe used a synthetic aperture radar to see features on the surface of Venus.

♦ The probe mapped 98 percent of the planet's surface over two years.

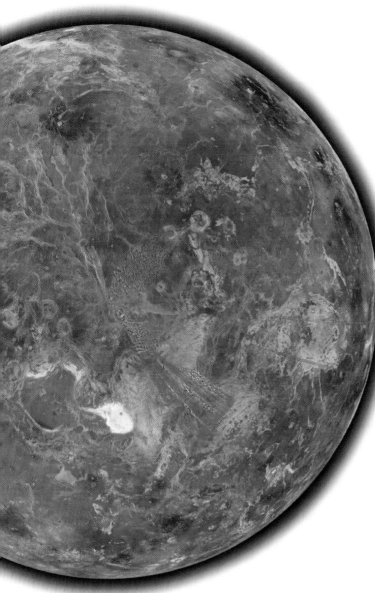

*A computer-simulated view of the planet Venus made up of radar images collected by* **Magellan.** *The image shows the planet's northern hemisphere.*

radar dish beamed radar signals down onto the ground in front of the signal. By combining the two signals, *Magellan* produced detailed radar maps in strips thousands of miles long and around 15 miles (25 km) across.

*Magellan* was scheduled for launch in 1988. It was delayed for a year when the space shuttle *Challenger* exploded in 1986 and all NASA's shuttle launches were put on hold. Because *Magellan* missed its launch window (the time when Venus is closest to Earth), it had to travel by a much longer route, taking 15 months to reach Venus and finally arriving in August 1990.

The probe went into an orbit that carried it over Venus's north and south poles so that it could map out long strips of the surface as the planet slowly rotated underneath it.

### Magellan's achievements

*Magellan* was a spectacular success, outlasting its intended lifetime, and mapping 98 percent of Venus's surface. *Magellan's* images revealed that, unlike Earth, Venus's outer crust is not split into plates floating around on top of a shifting mantle. The radar maps showed volcanoes and faults (which are often caused by moving plates on Earth) but no mountain ranges of the type pushed up when plates collide.

The radar mapping also revealed over 900 well-preserved impact craters on the planet's surface. Some scientists think these formed quite recently, so Venus must have been resurfaced by volcanoes in the past few hundred million years. (The Moon's highlands, which have not been disturbed for four billion years, are covered in millions of craters.)

Even when *Magellan* had finished its main work, it could still provide useful information. Between September 1992 and May 1993, the radar was switched off and the probe's telemetry (radio information about its exact position in space) was studied. When the probe flew over a region of Venus with higher or lower gravity, its course would deviate from a simple near-circular orbit, and NASA engineers were able to change these deviations into a map of the planet's gravity.

*Magellan* was also used to test techniques for use on future space probes. In May 1993, it dipped into the top layers of the atmosphere, using aerobraking (atmospheric resistance) to slow it down and put it in a lower orbit. After more aerobraking experiments, the probe was allowed to drop into the atmosphere completely in October 1994. It survived for about a day, and the telemetry it returned provided more information about the planet's atmosphere. Finally, the probe burned up completely—a spectacular end to a highly successful mission.

**CHECK THESE OUT!**
✔MARINER PROBE ✔NASA
✔PIONEER PROGRAM ✔VENUS

# Magma

**Molten material that rises from deep in Earth and solidifies as igneous rock**

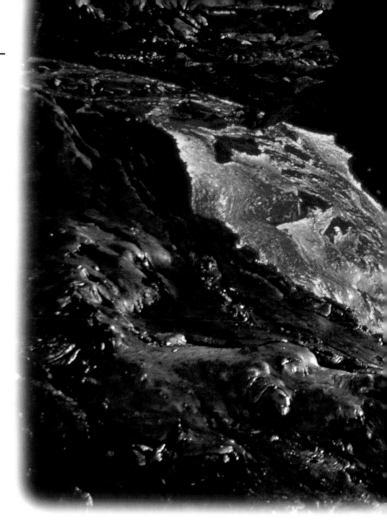

Much of Earth's crust is made of igneous rock. This is rock that has cooled and solidified from molten magma (MAG-muh) or lava. Magma is a mixture of gas, molten rock, and mineral crystals below the ground. When magma comes to the surface, it is called lava. Intrusive rocks such as granite (GRA-nuht) are formed when magma solidifies below ground. Extrusive rocks such as basalt (buh-SAWLT) are created when magma reaches the surface as lava.

## How magma is made

About 60 to 180 miles (100 to 300 km) below Earth's surface, there is a zone called the upper mantle. The pressure and temperature are so high there that rock does not behave as it does on Earth's surface. Because it is so near its melting point, the rock may break easily. This allows the plates that make up Earth's rigid outer layer to move about. At this depth, rock can melt and form magma. The melting point of the rock depends on its chemical composition and on the amount of liquid (usually water) present. All magmas are composed mainly of silicon and oxygen, which form a hard, glassy mineral called silica (SIH-lih-kuh).

## Types of magma

By studying the igneous rock formed when magma or lava solidifies, geologists (scientists who study the structure and history of rocks) have identified three different types of magma.

The continents of Earth contain rocks, such as granite, which are made of a type of magma high in silica. When this erupts from a volcano, rhyolite (RY-uh-LYT) lava is formed. This is a sticky type of lava that does not flow far and so creates steep-sided volcanoes. Continents also contain great quantities of andesite (AN-dih-ZYT) lava. It has less silica (55 to 65 percent) than the magma that forms granite and rhyolite. The ocean floors, on the other hand, are made of basalt (BAS-UHLT), a dense, low-silica lava. This lava is runny and forms low-sloping volcanoes.

---

# HIGHLIGHTS

◆ Magma is made in the upper mantle of Earth, deep below the crust.

◆ Magma is a fluid made of molten rock, mineral crystals, and gas.

◆ Magma can solidify deep in the crust to form intrusions or erupt as extrusive lava on the surface of Earth.

◆ As magma cools, a great variety of igneous rocks can form, such as granite and basalt.

◆ Minerals found in igneous rock include quartz, mica, and feldspar. Feldspar is the most common.

*Lava flow from Kilauea Volcano, Hawaii. Lava is magma that has erupted above the surface of the Earth. Lava can have different levels of viscosity (stickiness), creating different shapes of volcanoes.*

called batholiths (BA-thuh-LITHS) and are usually granite. Granite contains large crystals of quartz (KWARTZ), feldspar (FELD-SPAHR), and mica (MY-kuh). It is often cut and polished to be used in large slabs on building fronts.

Sills and dikes are smaller magma intrusions, usually only a few feet wide. Sills are sheets of magma that solidify along existing layers of rock, whereas dikes cut across the rock.

## Magma in the oceans

Nearly half of the volcanic activity on Earth happens in the ocean basins. As the crust is pulled apart, the mantle rock peridotite (a dense, dark rock) is partly melted, and basaltic magma forms. Some of this cools below the surface in huge intrusions of gabbro (a dark, coarse-grained igneous rock) and dikes. Much reaches the surface as basalt lava and erupts onto the seabed. Immediately, a skin of solidified lava forms, but the lava is still molten inside. As the molten lava moves, large pillow-shaped masses of lava are formed. This pillow lava is evidence of underwater eruptions.

## Magma in the continents

Basalt, andesite, and rhyolite magmas are all found on the continents. Where the continental crust is splitting, for example, along major rift systems, basalt wells up from the mantle. The heat from this may melt the crust and form rhyolite magma. An explosive eruption of frothy, gas-filled rhyolite lava forms rocks such as pumice (PUH-muhs) and obsidian (uhb-SIH-dee-uhn). Andesite magmas form where the ocean crust is partly melted. This occurs at the subduction zones. Here water can get caught up with the magma and lower its melting point. Andesitic volcanoes are explosive and form the classical cone-shaped mountains.

### CHECK THESE OUT!
✔FAULT ✔GEOLOGY ✔IGNEOUS ROCK ✔LANDFORM
✔PLATE TECTONICS ✔ROCK ✔VOLCANO

Basalt magma erupts at 2010 to 2190°F (1100 to 1200°C), whereas rhyolitic magma erupts at only 1470°F (800°C).

## Geological formations

Much magma comes to the surface along the midocean ridges, where the plates are moving apart a few inches each year. Here new crust is created as the magma solidifies along the ridge.

Around the rim of the Pacific Ocean, there are subduction zones where an ocean plate is being pushed below a continental plate. The descending plate melts at great depth. This creates magma that rises up into the continental crust, forming intrusions (magma that solidified underground) and volcanoes, such as along the Andes Mountains. In the continents, and especially where there are high mountain ranges, magma slowly cools and crystallizes at great depths. Giant blisters of magma, often thousands of miles across, form here. Gradually the magma invades the existing rocks, surrounding large areas and melting it. This process may take millions of years. The largest intrusions are

# Magnesium

**A light, reactive metal used to make high-strength alloys**

The alkaline earth metals make up group 2 (IIA) of the periodic table. Magnesium is one of these highly reactive metals and, like the others, reacts readily with other elements to form compounds. As a result, magnesium is only found in nature combined with other elements.

Magnesium gets its name from the ore magnesia (magnesium oxide, $MgO$), which in turn is named after Magnesia, a district in ancient Greece where the ore was discovered. The pure metal was first isolated from this compound in 1808 by British chemist Humphry Davy (1778–1829). Davy obtained magnesium as an amalgam (a mixture with mercury) by the electrolysis of magnesia. This involves using an electrical current to decompose the compound into its elements. Davy used mercury in the process, so as the magnesium metal formed, it dissolved in the mercury. After electrolysis, Davy evaporated the mercury to produce pure metallic magnesium. In 1833, British chemist and physicist Michael Faraday (1791–1867) isolated pure magnesium from molten magnesium chloride ($MgCl_2$) by electrolysis. Faraday's method is still used to manufacture magnesium.

## How magnesium is used

Magnesium is a silver-white metal that looks similar to aluminum but is a third less dense. This lightness makes it ideal for use in building aircraft and automobiles. These vehicles must be made with strong, light materials in order to use fuel efficiently. Pure magnesium is not particularly strong and tends to snap. However, its properties can be greatly improved when combined in alloys (mixtures) with other metals. The majority of magnesium produced by industry goes to make alloys.

Some other uses for magnesium stem from the light and heat it produces when it burns in air. Magnesium powder burns with a brief but intense flash when ignited. This made it useful for early flash photography. During World War II (1939–1945), magnesium was used to make bombs, as the combustion of the magnesium generated enough heat to set fire to the bombed target. Magnesium is still used in fireworks, flares, solid rocket fuels, and blasting powders.

## Magnesium from seawater

Magnesium is present in seawater as dissolved magnesium salts. On average, a gallon of seawater contains almost ¼ oz (6 g) of the

*Magnesium is a very reactive metal. When lit, it burns with an intense white light, generating clouds of white smoke.*

---

## HIGHLIGHTS

◆ Magnesium is a member of group 2 (IIA) of the periodic table—the alkaline earth metals.

◆ Magnesium is present in chlorophyll, the green pigment in plants.

◆ Strong, lightweight magnesium alloys are used to build aircraft and automobiles.

metal. As the oceans are immense and water is easy to pump, many magnesium manufacturers use seawater as a raw material, even though it takes almost 800 tons (726 tonnes) of seawater to produce a single ton (0.9 tonne) of magnesium.

In the first stage of the process, seawater is pumped into an artificial lagoon and treated with a base to produce magnesium hydroxide ($Mg(OH)_2$). The hydroxide is insoluble in water, so it forms a slurry (a thin mixture of fine material) on the floor of the lagoon. This slurry is collected and reacted with hydrochloric acid to produce magnesium chloride ($MgCl_2$). Water is evaporated from the solution to form solid magnesium chloride, which is then heated to dry it out. In the final stage, dry magnesium chloride is heated to around 1300°F (700°C), when it becomes liquid. Electrolyzing (passing an electrical current through) the molten salt produces magnesium metal and chlorine gas. The metal floats to the top of the molten magnesium chloride and can be run off.

## Magnesium from minerals

Magnesium is the sixth most abundant metal found on Earth, making up about 2.5 percent of the Earth's crust. The most common ores of magnesium are dolomite and magnesite. There are major U.S. reserves of these ores in California and Nevada, and magnesium ores are also mined in Austria, Canada, China, India, Russia, and South America.

Magnesium is extracted from dolomite by first roasting the ore. The mixture produced is then heated with coke and chlorine to form magnesium chloride. This can be electrolyzed to form pure magnesium.

## Reactions with air and water

Group 2 (IIA) metals are less reactive than group 1 (IA) elements, such as sodium, but more reactive than most metals. Magnesium tarnishes (reacts with oxygen) slowly in air at room temperature, forming a layer of oxide. The pure metal is often stored in kerosene to protect it from exposure to the air.

## EVERYDAY SCIENCE

### Magnesium in Alloys
Magnesium alloys are useful where strength and lightness are required, such as in components (parts) for aircraft, automobiles, and suitcases. A component made from a good magnesium alloy is as strong as a steel component but has less than one-fifth of its weight. The most common alloying metals for magnesium are aluminum, manganese, and zinc. These metals improve the strength of magnesium and make it easier to cast and shape. Magnesium also improves the properties of other metals. Commercial aluminum is strengthened by a content of up to 5 percent magnesium.

Heating magnesium ribbon in air causes it to burn fiercely with an intense white light. The product is magnesium oxide, which appears as clouds of white smoke. Once lit, the ribbon continues to burn unaided. Magnesium does not react with cold water and so can be used underwater in warning flares. When heated with boiling water, however, it reacts with the steam to form magnesium hydroxide and hydrogen gas.

## Medicinal compounds

Compounds of magnesium have a huge range of medicinal uses. Magnesium carbonate ($MgCO_3$) is used as a filler for diluting cosmetics and medicinal drugs. Magnesium sulfate, which is better known as Epsom salts, is a laxative used to treat complaints such as constipation. Milk of magnesia, commonly taken to ease indigestion, is magnesium hydroxide mixed with water.

Magnesium is an important part of certain organic compounds, such as chlorophyll (the green pigment in plants). It is also essential to the way the human body uses carbohydrates. It is present in the skeleton, teeth, soft tissue, and body fluids. Magnesium is a vital part of the diet of all animals, and it is found in a wide range of foods such as cereals, vegetables, nuts, meat, and dairy products.

### CHECK THESE OUT!
✔ACID AND BASE ✔ALLOY ✔ELEMENT ✔METAL

# Magnetic Pole

## A point near Earth's axis of rotation where the magnetic force is vertical

At different times of night, or at different times throughout the year, the groups of stars in the sky seem to have moved. This is because Earth rotates about its axis every 24 hours and also moves on its long orbit around the Sun. There is one star that always remains in the same place in the northern sky. This is Polaris, the North Star. For many centuries, this star was the only guide that travelers could use to find their way at night.

The Chinese were the first to discover a magnetic compass that pointed toward the North Star, even when the star was hidden by clouds. It was a long time before this discovery reached Europe, and longer still before it was fully understood. Late in the 16th century, Dr. William Gilbert (1544–1603) explained that Earth was a magnet with a North Pole at one end (so-called because it attracted the north pole of a compass) and a South Pole at its other end.

The geographic North and South Poles mark the ends of the axis about which Earth rotates, and this axis points very nearly to Polaris.

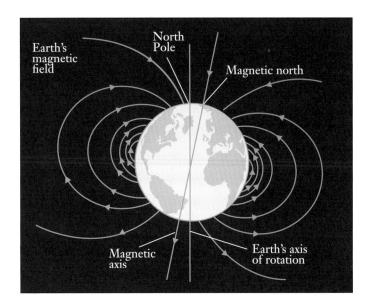

*Earth has a magnetic field around it with north and south magnetic poles, just like that of a bar magnet. These poles are close to the geographic poles.*

However, explorers (Columbus was one of the first) discovered that their compasses did not always point directly toward Polaris. One of the reasons for this is that although the north and south magnetic poles are in the polar regions, they do not coincide with the geographic poles.

A more complicated reason is that Earth's structure can also change the direction in which a compass points. The angle between the direction the compass points and true north is called magnetic declination. This can vary dramatically, depending on where in the world the compass is being used.

Because Earth is a magnet, it has a field of magnetic force around it. The magnetic lines of force curve from the south magnetic pole to the north magnetic pole, just like those between the poles of a bar magnet. The north pole of a free-hanging magnetic needle will be attracted toward the North Pole. At the equator, the needle will be horizontal. However, nearer to the North Pole, it will dip toward the ground. At the north magnetic pole, it will point vertically downward. This is called magnetic inclination.

## HIGHLIGHTS

◆ The North and South Poles are at the ends of Earth's axis, but the magnetic poles are not.

◆ The north magnetic pole is some 800 miles (1,288 km) from the geographic North Pole, and the south magnetic pole is some 1,600 miles (2,574 km) from the geographic South Pole.

◆ Earth's magnetism is produced by movement of the deep liquid core.

◆ Solar winds interact with Earth's magnetic field, producing auroras (northern and southern lights).

At present, the north magnetic pole is at a latitude of about 73 degrees north and a longitude of about 102 degrees west. It is located in the Northwest Territories of Canada near Bathurst Island, between the Arctic Ocean and Baffin Bay. This is about 800 miles (1,288 km) from the geographic North Pole. The south magnetic pole is just off the coast of Antarctica in the southern Indian Ocean, at about 67 degrees south and about 143 degrees east. This is around 1,600 miles (2,574 km) from the South Pole.

## The geodynamo

At Earth's center is a hot and dense solid inner core. Surrounding this is a liquid core at about 9000°F (4982°C). Both cores are rich in iron and nickel. Scientists explain Earth's magnetism by comparing it to a dynamo (an electrical generator). As Earth rotates, the liquid core

*Magnetite is a magnetic mineral. After it has been heated and cooled, magnetite realigns itself with the Earth's magnetic field.*

moves like electricity flowing through a coil of wire. This flow of electricity produces magnetic forces. They emerge from one end of the coil and loop through space to the other end.

Earth's magnetic field is called the magnetosphere. It can extend up to 30,000 miles (48,270 km) into space. On the side nearer the Sun, it is closer to Earth. On the opposite side, it stretches into a tail, so the magnetosphere is shaped rather like a comet. The distorted shape of the magnetosphere is caused by a stream of charged particles from the Sun, called the solar wind. Above the north and south magnetic poles, the solar wind causes electrical disturbances. Oxygen atoms in Earth's upper atmosphere shine with a green light, and nitrogen atoms shine red. This is the cause of the auroras—the northern and southern lights—that flicker in the night skies at 60 to 600 miles (97 to 970 km) above Earth's surface. The colored light rays and arcs of the auroras can be seen throughout the Arctic and Antarctic regions, and even farther afield.

## Fossil magnetism

Scientists have discovered that Earth's magnetic field has changed many times over millions of years. Magnetic minerals, particularly iron ores such as magnetite and hematite, lose their magnetism at high temperatures but become magnetic again as they cool down. As a flow of volcanic lava cools, the magnetite and hematite in it will therefore align themselves (fall into line) with Earth's magnetic field. In a similar way, sediments containing magnetic minerals will align as they become trapped in rock formations.

A study of geological deposits formed during the last 7,000 years has shown that the position of the magnetic poles has wandered around a region within 11 degrees near the geographic poles. This is because of the movement of the continental landmasses.

More surprisingly, the magnetic poles themselves have reversed completely at least 20 times in the last 10 million years. This discovery is important in dating rocks. It also provides evidence that supports theories about the way the ocean floor is spreading. Molten rock cools as it moves away from each side of a midocean ridge. The magnetic material trapped in the ridge is a record of the magnetic direction at the time. As the magnetic direction reverses, it produces a succession of magnetic stripes that can be used to piece together geological history.

### CHECK THESE OUT!
✔EARTH ✔ELECTROMAGNETISM ✔MAGNETISM

# Magnetism

**The force that is produced by the movement of electric charges**

More than 2,000 years ago, the Chinese discovered that a piece of a certain shiny black mineral would always point toward the North Star (Pole Star) if it was hung from a thread. However, it was probably Arab sailors who realized the importance of this discovery for navigating (finding their way). After many centuries, this information reached the West. There, the mineral came to be called magnetite because it was found in a part of Greece named Magnesia. In English, it was called lodestone.

The first scientific study of magnetism in Europe was written in 1269 by Pierre de Maricourt (known as Peter the Pilgrim). He described the properties of the lodestone and how, by stroking the lodestone along an iron needle, the needle would become magnetized. He named the end of the magnet that pointed

## HIGHLIGHTS

◆ A magnet has a north and a south pole.

◆ A magnetic field is represented by the lines of force between the two poles.

◆ The force between two magnetic poles decreases in proportion to the square of the distance between them.

◆ Ferromagnetic materials are easily magnetized.

*When the like poles of two bar magnets are aligned, their magnetic fields repel each other. Scattered iron filings line up, showing the two magnetic fields.*

north its north pole, and the other its south pole. He reported how two north or south poles would repel (push away) each other, while unlike poles would attract each other. He also described how a magnet could be used to find a direction by floating it on a piece of wood in water.

De Maricourt also suggested ways of placing a magnet on a pivot (PIH-vuht; a fixed pin on which something turns). Later, navigators placed a circle of paper under the pivoted magnet, with radiating lines pointing in 32 directions. To compass means to enclose in a circle, and so this diagram was called a compass rose.

During the late Middle Ages, explorers found the lodestone essential. Whatever direction the winds blew, they always knew which way was north, even if the North Star was hidden by clouds. It was not until 1600 that English physician William Gilbert (1544–1603) published the results of his experiments in magnetism. He concluded that Earth itself was a giant magnet, and he shaped a lodestone into a sphere to demonstrate this. Italian scientist Galileo Galilei (1564–1642) greatly admired Gilbert's methods, and the book was a scientific bestseller.

## Magnetism and electricity

Early scientists realized that there was a similarity between magnetic and electrostatic forces. In both cases, like repels like, while like attracts unlike. In 1785, French physicist Charles-Augustin de Coulomb (1736–1806) showed that both magnetic and electrostatic forces obey the same rule. The force between two magnetic poles or two electrically charged bodies lessened in proportion to the square of the distance between them.

The next step did not come until the invention of the electric battery in 1800 by Italian physicist Alessandro Volta (1745–1827). In 1820, Danish physicist Hans Ørsted (1777–1851) discovered that electric current flowing in a wire would deflect a compass needle placed beside it.

In France, André-Marie Ampère (1775–1836) learned of this discovery and began to experiment. He found that two wires carrying current in the same direction attracted one another but repelled each other if the currents were flowing in opposite directions. He also

# DISCOVERERS

## William Gilbert

English physician William Gilbert (1544–1603) was a leading doctor in England. Queen Elizabeth I was one of his patients. Gilbert spent much time studying the properties of the lodestone. His report, published in 1600, was the first scientific study of magnets since that of Peter the Pilgrim in the 13th century.

*This engraving shows William Gilbert hammering metal in his workshop.*

Gilbert's book had the title *De Magnete* (*About Magnetics*). He began by dismissing superstitions about lodestones, such as the belief that they could cure disease. Next, he explained how magnetic attraction and repulsion were different from that between substances, like amber, that had been rubbed. He went on to suggest that Earth itself is a giant magnet. He explained why compass needles point north and described ways of making magnets. He also proposed that a magnet's properties came from an invisible "orb of virtue" surrounding it. This was the first idea of the existence of a magnetic field.

found that a wire coiled into the shape of a spring had a north and south pole just like a magnet. When a steel needle was placed inside the coil, the needle became magnetized.

Ampère suggested that the deflection of a compass needle could be used to measure the strength of an electric current. This is the basis

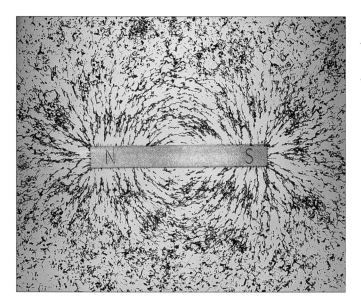

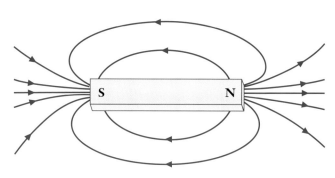

*The magnetic forces of a bar magnet flow in loops from the north to the south pole (below). Iron filings scattered around the bar magnet line up with these forces (left), showing the shape of the magnetic field.*

of the galvanometer, an instrument that measures the strength of an electric current.

In 1825, English scientist William Sturgeon (1783–1850) made the first electromagnet. He wound a wire 18 times around a horseshoe-shaped piece of iron. When a current passed through the wire, the horseshoe would lift iron weighing more than 20 times its own weight.

If a sheet of paper is laid over a magnet and sprinkled with tiny iron filings, the filings line up to follow curved lines of force between the magnet's two poles. English scientist Michael Faraday (1791–1867) showed that, in the same way, magnetic lines of force—a magnetic field—formed in circles around a wire carrying a current. In 1821, he built a piece of equipment that allowed a magnet to rotate around a wire, or the wire to rotate around the magnet. This led to the development of the electric motor.

From his experiments, Faraday argued that it should be possible to produce electric current in a wire by magnetism. In 1831, he achieved this by winding two coils of wire around an iron bar. One was connected to a battery, to make the bar a magnet. The other was connected to a galvanometer (machine that measures an electric current). When the battery was switched on, magnetizing the iron bar, the galvanometer's needle moved, showing that an electric current was running through the second wire. Faraday realized that it was the changing magnetic field in the bar that produced the current shown on the

galvanometer. This was discovered at the same time by U.S. physicist Joseph Henry (1797–1878), who did not publish his findings until later. Modern electrical generators are based on this effect.

Faraday's experiments and discoveries helped to bring electricity into the modern world, but he had only vague theories about the relation between magnetism and electricity. It was Scottish physicist James Clerk Maxwell (1831–1879) who followed up Faraday's work. He showed that electric and magnetic fields travel together through space as waves of electromagnetic radiation.

In 1905, German-born U.S. physicist Albert Einstein (1879–1955) published his theory of relativity. He showed conclusively that magnetism and electricity are both aspects of one common phenomenon (a fact or event).

### How a magnet is made

Ampère suggested that a material was magnetic because it contained tiny loops of electric current in its structure, and this was partly correct. Each of the electrons circling the nucleus of an atom forms a loop of electric current, so each will produce its own magnetic field.

Usually, inside the atom, these magnetic fields will cancel each other out. However, in some atoms, they combine. Iron, nickel, and cobalt are the best known of the elements that show this effect (called ferromagnetism), and they are easily magnetized. Groups of individual atoms line up together to form tiny magnetic regions called domains (doh-MAYNZ). Inside a normal piece of metal, however, these domains are usually pointing in different directions.

To make a magnet from a piece of iron, many of the domains must be lined up in the same direction. This can be done by stroking the piece of iron with a magnet, or by placing it inside a coil carrying a current. A sensitive microphone can pick up the clicking and hissing noises made by domains lining up. Even Earth's magnetism can be used to magnetize a ferromagnetic (easily magnetized) material. If an iron rod is placed in line with Earth's magnetic field and hit with a hammer, the force is enough to cause some of the domains to line up. A ready-made magnet needs careful handling or its domains may be knocked out of place and take on the direction of Earth's

magnetic field, rather than keeping the north and south poles of the magnet intact.

Heat can also destroy a magnet. The atoms gain energy and vibrate more freely, so that the domains move out of alignment.

The strength of magnetism that a material can develop is called its permeability (PUHR-mee-uh-BIH-luh-tee). Nickel's permeability is 40, cobalt's is 55, iron's is over 1,000. This is why many magnets are made mainly of iron. The mineral magnetite is a natural oxide of iron. Some alloys that do not contain iron, however, make even stronger magnets. One of these, alnico, is made of aluminum, nickel, and cobalt.

## Making magnets

Iron and the other ferromagnetic metals are used to make magnets for different uses. Nearly pure iron is called soft iron. It is easily magnetized by

## LOOK CLOSER

### Magnetic Storms

The magnetic field around Earth is called the magnetosphere. It reaches as far as 30,000 miles (48,270 km) out into space and interacts with the solar wind. This is a stream of electrically charged particles that blows away from the Sun at a speed of about 240 miles per second (386 km/s). Like a giant generator, the interaction produces electric currents high in Earth's atmosphere.

Sometimes the solar wind blows in gusts, rather like a windstorm on Earth. Powerful new electric currents swirl about in the magnetosphere. Their effects are often seen as spectacular auroras (northern or southern lights), and they also interfere with radio, television, and radar. Communications and navigation are interrupted. Electric power grids can also be affected, and this sometimes results in massive blackouts.

Like Earth, the Sun has a magnetic field. However, the Sun does not have a rigid surface like Earth, and its magnetic field is in constant motion. Sunspots are concentrations of this field. They look dark because they are much cooler than the rest of the surface. They are each about twice the size of Earth and last for a week or more.

*Gases on the Sun's surface loop in line with the Sun's powerful magnetic field.*

The number of sunspots rises and falls through an 11-year cycle. Magnetic storms are connected with the appearance of sunspots on the Sun's surface, and they follow a similar 11-year pattern. They can last from several hours to as much as ten days. Similar dark spots have been seen on other stars as well as the Sun.

# EVERYDAY SCIENCE

## Maglev Trains

Magnetically levitated (maglev) trains can reach speeds of more than 300 miles per hour (483 km/h). They may soon be able to compete with air transportation over shorter distances. These trains are not driven by the friction of wheels on tracks. They float silently along a single guide track, on a magnetic cushion. The track is fitted with electromagnetic coils along its length. Other electromagnets inside the train are attracted to the coil ahead and repelled by the coil behind. The current in each coil is rapidly reversed so that the train is pulled and pushed forward at the same time. All the while, magnetic repulsion keeps the train floating above the track. The first maglev trains are already operating in Germany, Japan, and Australia.

*This maglev train in Sydney, Australia, floats a fraction of an inch above the magnetic track.*

an electric field but loses most of its magnetism as soon as the current is switched off or reversed. This property is very valuable for making solenoids (SOH-luh-NOYDZ; a soft iron core inside a coil of wire). Solenoids are magnetic switches used when an electric current needs to be switched on and off rapidly. For example, the starter motor of a car needs a large current to turn it, but once the engine has fired, the current is no longer needed. Turning the ignition key allows a current to flow through the solenoid switch. This magnetizes the solenoid, which in turn closes a switch that fires the engine. When the ignition key is released, the iron core loses its magnetism. It falls back, breaks the circuit, and the starter stops turning.

Electromagnets can also be used for lifting and moving heavy pieces of iron and steel. The heavy load can be released from the lifting magnet and placed down by switching off the magnetizing current.

Permanent magnets retain their magnetism once the magnetizing current has been removed. They are made from steel and steel alloys. In these metals, unlike in soft iron, the domains become fixed in position once they are lined up. Permanent magnets are used in some types of electric motors, generators, and loudspeakers. They are also useful for laboratory experiments and are often bar-shaped or horseshoe-shaped. In a horseshoe magnet, the lines of force run only a short distance between the north and south poles, and the magnetic field is very strong.

## Magnetohydrodynamics

In an electric motor, the current flows through wire coils. The coils generate a magnetic field and, where this intersects with the fixed magnetic field of a magnet, the coils are made to turn. A stream of charged particles in a fluid can be used instead of a wire. This is the basis of the new science of magnetohydrodynamics (MHD).

MHD ideas have enabled scientists to find a way to power ships using seawater. Salt water contains charged particles. When salt water is pumped between strong magnets, the water accelerates and provides a driving force. A small craft, the Japanese *Yamoto*, reached 6 miles per hour (9.7 km/h) in 1992 using this method.

Plasma is a gas that has been heated to such a temperature that it breaks up into charged particles. If a stream of plasma is forced through a magnetic field at high speed, it will generate a large electric current. Such an MHD generator is very efficient and may become a central part of commercial power supplies.

### CHECK THESE OUT!

✔ELECTRICITY ✔ELECTROMAGNETISM
✔ELECTRON ✔ELECTROSTATICS ✔MAGNETIC POLE

# Manganese

**A brittle transition metal used to harden steel**

Manganese is a hard, silver-white metal. It was discovered and isolated as a metal in 1774 by Swedish chemists Carl Scheele (1742–1786) and Johan Gahn (1745–1818), who extracted the metal by heating its oxide ore with carbon. Manganese forms an unusually wide range of chemical compounds, although few of them are used on a large scale.

## Extraction from ores

Manganese is the 12th most common element in Earth's crust, making up around 0.1 percent of the mass of the crust. Pyrolusite, which is a form of manganese dioxide ($MnO_2$), is important for manganese production. This is changed into ferromanganese (a mixture of iron and manganese) by heating manganese and iron oxides with coke in a blast furnace. The product is in a form that can be used for making steel. A more expensive method makes manganese by the electrolysis of manganese sulfate ($MnSO_4$), which forms when pyrolusite reacts with hot concentrated sulfuric acid. This method is used to make pure manganese for making alloys with metals other than iron.

Vast reserves of manganese lie in nodules on the ocean floor. Some nodules contain up to 24 percent manganese by weight. The cost of retrieving nodules from the ocean, however, makes them an impractical source of manganese.

## Chemical compounds

Manganese is a transition element in group 7 (VIIB) of the periodic table. It can have oxidation states between –3 and 7, which means that it can formally accept as many as three electrons or donate up to seven to other atoms when it forms compounds. The higher oxidation states happen in its compounds with oxygen. In manganese (II) oxide (MnO), manganese loses two electrons to form the $Mn^{2+}$ ion. In the manganate (VII) ion (permanganate; $MnO^{4-}$), it shares seven electrons. Manganese (IV) oxide is used to improve the efficiency of zinc–carbon cells, and potassium permanganate ($KMnO_4$) is an

*This photograph of the floor of the Northeast Atlantic Ocean shows a field of manganese nodules.*

important oxidizing agent in the chemical industry. The lower oxidation states are rare. The –3 rate occurs in $Mn(NO_3)CO$, and the –2 state in an anion (negatively charged ion) formed with the large organic molecule phthalocyanine.

## Uses of the metal

Almost all the manganese produced by industry is used for making alloys with other metals—mainly with iron. Alloys of manganese with iron are used in the preparation of steel. Adding manganese to crude molten steel removes any sulfur as manganese sulfide. This can be removed from the surface of the steel. If sulfur were not removed, the steel would break apart when rolled at high temperatures. Adding around 12 percent manganese to steel forms an exceptionally hard alloy called Hadfield steel. This alloy is used to make bank safes, machine tools, and rails for railroad switches. Pure manganese can be alloyed with copper, tin, and zinc to make manganese bronze, which resists seawater corrosion and is useful for making ship propellers. Small amounts of manganese are added to copper, magnesium, and aluminum to increase their strengths.

**CHECK THESE OUT!**
✔ALLOY ✔BATTERY ✔IRON AND STEEL

# Maps and Mapping

**The process of making maps, graphic representations of part or all of Earth's surface**

People use maps showing roads and buildings to find out where they are and how to get from one place to another. Maps are also used to show many kinds of other information, such as geological features, soil types, regions of different vegetation, and the relative heights of different areas.

Mapmakers are called cartographers. People have been making maps of various kinds since ancient times by drawing lines on the ground or on silk, clay, paper, or parchment. Today, maps and atlases (collections of maps) are published as leaflets, books, or on computer software.

Before a map can be drawn up, detailed information about the area must be gathered, either by survey teams working at the location

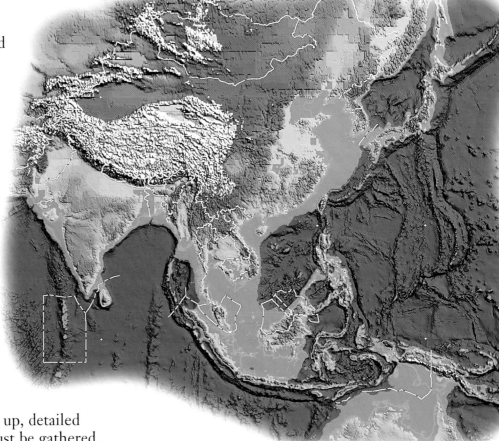

*A map of Asia showing physical and political features. Different colors show the relief of the land, and white lines show political boundaries.*

or from satellite pictures. Maps have improved as the instruments for gathering the required information have become more accurate.

## Types of maps

Different types of maps have different functions. Political maps show the boundaries of countries, while route maps help people to find their way. Railroad and subway maps are simplified to show information at a glance. They show the sequence of station stops on the line but not the geographical location of the stations.

---

## HIGHLIGHTS

♦ Maps are geographical layouts of part or all of Earth's surface.

♦ Maps have been made all over the world since ancient times.

♦ Symbols and scales used on maps help to show information clearly and simply.

♦ Some distortion is unavoidable when Earth's curved surface is represented on a flat map.

Geological maps show the rocks of an area. Weather maps generally use symbols to represent clouds, snow, rain, and other weather patterns. Air pressure is shown by lines called isobars (EYE-soh-BAHRZ) that connect areas of equal pressure. Weather fronts are often shown as darker lines, with triangles and semicircles showing the direction in which the front is moving. Triangles are used for a cold front, semicircles for a warm front. Sailors use detailed nautical charts showing oceans and coastlines to navigate at sea. Nautical charts also show the depth of the seabed and underwater features such as hidden reefs and safe anchorages.

## History of maps and mapping

Maps have been made since ancient times, even by people who had no written language. The ancient Mesopotamians were the earliest-known mapmakers. A clay tablet found in Iraq, dating back to 2500 B.C.E., shows streams, settlements, and hills and identifies north, east, and west. In the 2nd century B.C.E., Chinese cartographers painted maps on silk and wove a faint grid into them. In ancient Greece at that time, the geographer Eratosthenes (EH-ruh-TOHS-thuh-neez) drew a world map that included parallel lines running from east to west. Fifty years later, north–south lines were added to maps to form a grid. In the 2nd century C.E., Greek cartographer Ptolemy (TOH-luh-mee) included a world map and 26 regional maps in his book *Geographia*.

Ptolemy used the terms *latitude* and *longitude* in his work. Latitude is the distance in degrees north or south of the equator (where the latitude is 0 degrees). Longitude is the distance east or west of the Prime Meridian (longitude 0 degrees). The Prime Meridian is also called the Greenwich Meridian because it runs through Greenwich, England. Lines of latitude, therefore, run around the globe east to west, and lines of longitude run north to south.

## LOOK CLOSER

# Mapmakers and Their Projections

Since ancient times, cartographers have been aware of the difficulties of showing the curved surface of the Earth on a flat map. Over the years, mapmakers have used many different projections to try to reduce the distortion involved. One of the projections most widely used for world maps is Mercator's projection, which was devised by Gerardus Mercator in the 16th century.

Mercator's projection shows the shapes of the continents accurately but distorts scale, exaggerating distances toward the North Pole. This makes countries in the far north, such as Greenland, look much larger than they really are. In the 1970s, cartographer Arno Peters devised a new projection, which now bears his name. Peters's projection distorts the shapes of continents but shows their true size.

Another type of projection used for world maps are equal-area (homolographic) projections. All parts of the globe are shown on the map to the same scale. The Prime Meridian is shown as a straight line, but other lines of longitude curve increasingly toward the edges of the map. In some versions of this projection, cuts are made along lines of longitude to spread the map out, which further reduces distortion.

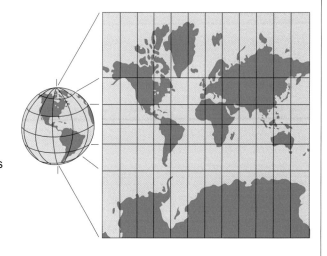

*Mercator's map (like the one above) makes the polar regions look too big. Equal-area projections (below) distort the shape of the continents slightly.*

*Satellite images of Earth's surface are used to produce highly accurate maps.*

After Greek times, maps made little progress in Europe until around 1300. At that time, reasonable charts of harbors and waterways were available for sailors, but land maps and world maps were still based on Ptolemy's maps or on legends. During the 16th century, the discoveries made by Christopher Columbus (1451–1506) and other explorers led to a new interest in maps.

The invention of printing made it easier to produce maps more quickly. Flemish geographer Gerardus Mercator (1512–1594) was a very successful mapmaker. In the late 17th century, maps improved through the use of a new surveying technique called triangulation. By the 18th century, an instrument for accurately measuring angles, called a theodolite (thee-OD-uh-LYT), was in use. Modern land survey teams still use the same tools and techniques.

The 19th century brought the first accurate maps of whole countries. The 20th century saw great advances in mapmaking. Aerial photography began during World War I (1914–1918). The arrival of satellites in the 1960s meant Earth's surface could be seen from space for the first time. Satellite sensors send images to ground stations where they are made into maps.

Today's satellites may also use radar or measure infrared radiation to produce detailed maps or ones that show soil type or vegetation cover. Advances in deep-sea echo sounders now make it possible to map the ocean floor.

## Reading maps

Maps must be uncluttered and easy to read. Symbols are used to save space and to show information clearly. The symbols used on a map are explained in a key at the side.

Some map symbols are so commonly used that they may not be shown in the key. Height above sea level is often represented by different background colors: green for lowland areas, brown for higher ground, blue for water, and white for ice and snow. Boundaries between countries or regions are shown by lines; a thicker line indicates a more important boundary. Major and minor roads are shown in the same way.

Relief, the lie of the land and the height above sea level, is shown on physical maps by contour lines, which connect points at the same height. Spot heights give the exact height of a specific hill or mountain. The closer the spacing between contour lines, the steeper the terrain.

Many maps are divided into squares by a grid. Each square is labeled with a number and letter (coordinates) to allow readers to find a place on the map easily. More detailed coordinates are used to pinpoint a location exactly.

Every map has a scale key to show the distance on Earth's surface that is represented by one unit on the map. A scale of 1:25,000 indicates that each unit (for example, one inch) on the map represents 25,000 times the same unit on the ground.

Map scales are described as large and small. These terms refer to the size of the fraction used in the scale, not to the size of the area covered by the map. Large scales, such as 1:10,000, are often used for maps that show relatively small areas such as city centers. Small scales, for example 1:50,000,000, are used to map very large areas, such as the entire Pacific Ocean.

### CHECK THESE OUT!
✔EARTH ✔REMOTE SENSING
✔UNITED STATES GEOLOGICAL SURVEY

# Marine Exploration

## The study of the underwater world

Almost three-quarters of Earth's surface is covered by water. Since ancient times, people have been fascinated by the mysteries of the deep. Records from 4500 B.C.E. tell of divers in the Mediterranean Sea. By 1300 B.C.E., divers may have been using goggles made of polished tortoiseshell to search the seabed. Without breathing equipment, divers with strong lungs could swim down to depths of 100 feet (30 m) below the water surface but no deeper.

From the late 1700s, early scientists began to develop breathing equipment that used compressed air to explore the undersea world. Compressed air is air that is put under pressure so that plenty of it can be contained in a fairly small cylinder on a diver's back. Early divers wore clumsy canvas suits and big copper helmets and were connected to a boat by a long air hose and a lifeline so they could be hauled to safety.

In his classic novel *Twenty Thousand Leagues Under the Sea*, Jules Verne (1828–1905) described people using portable breathing equipment to explore the seas. In 1943, French naval officer Jacques-Yves Cousteau (1910–1997) helped to

*This deep sea diver is counting the number of reef fish he finds underwater.*

---

## HIGHLIGHTS

◆ Compressed air equipment for undersea exploration was developed in the late 1700s.

◆ During the 1870s, scientists on board the British research ship *Challenger* proved that life existed in the deep oceans.

◆ Submarines developed rapidly during World War I, when the invention of sonar made it possible to map the ocean floor.

◆ Marine exploration is carried out by gas and oil prospectors, drug companies, and many others.

---

develop the aqualung, an underwater breathing apparatus that included a tank of compressed air strapped to the diver's back. This new invention was similar to the system Verne had imagined. Today, such equipment is often called scuba, meaning "self-contained underwater breathing apparatus." Thousands of tourists as well as scientists now regularly put on masks, fins, and air tanks to explore the wonders of the deep.

Using scuba equipment with highly pressurized air, professional divers have reached depths of 1,970 feet (600 m). However, such deep dives can be dangerous because the increasing water pressure can force gases such as nitrogen to enter the divers' bloodstream. If they return to the surface too quickly, the nitrogen forms tiny bubbles that block the normal blood circulation. Decompression sickness, or the bends, results. This condition is very painful and can be fatal.

## Early marine exploration

From the 15th century onward, European sailors set out across the oceans to discover new lands and claim them for their countries. Knowledge of the oceans and coastal waters became very important. During the 17th century, a British scientific institution called the Royal Society began systematically to gather data on the seas. Whenever ships set out on a long voyage, captains were asked to make a record of water depths, ocean currents, and salt levels in the seas through which they sailed.

In 1724, Italian geologist Luigi Marsili (1658–1730) published the first systematic study of the sea. Through a series of measurements off

*This is one of the first photographs taken underwater. It was made in 1893 by French zoologist Louis Boutan using a magnesium flash.*

the south coast of France, Marsili drew an underwater map that showed the shallow coastal waters dropping off to deeper depths. The term *soundings* is frequently used for simple depth measurements carried out with ropes and similar devices. A weighted rope with some tallow (animal fat) fixed in a hollow in the lead weight has been used by sailors in the past. The tallow would pick up particles of sand if there was a sandy bottom, or nothing if the seabed was rocky. The rope would be marked off at depth intervals with pieces of ribbon. Marsili also recorded the salt levels, water temperatures, currents, and tides in the Mediterranean Sea.

Navigation in the open oceans remained difficult. Sailors navigating out of sight of land used the position of the Sun at midday and the Moon and stars at night to plot their location. However, they needed accurate clocks to know when midday had arrived, and on cloudy nights they could not see the Moon and stars. In the late 18th century, John Harrison (1693–1776), a British carpenter turned watchmaker, made the first accurate clocks that could also be used at sea. They were tested by, among others, Captain James Cook (1728–1779), who made many important marine discoveries and recorded ocean depths throughout the Pacific Ocean.

U.S. statesman and scientist Benjamin Franklin (1706–1790) was another early marine explorer. During eight voyages between America and Europe, he discovered the Gulf Stream, the warm current that flows northward along the east coast of the United States.

While sailors gathered information that helped with ocean navigation, little was known about marine plant and animal life. In the 1840s, English naturalist Edward Forbes (1815–1854) published his theory that the ocean depths below 1,800 feet (550 m) contained no animal life. In 1859, English naturalist Charles Darwin (1809–1882) published his revolutionary book on evolution, *The Origin of Species*. Darwin stated that evolution occurred more slowly in the sea than on land because conditions in the oceans remained more constant.

In 1868, Scottish scientist Charles Wyville Thomson (1830–1882) challenged Forbes's idea that the ocean depths were lifeless. He dredged

## Discovering Shipwrecks

The lure of sunken riches has long attracted treasure-seekers to shipwrecks. In 1687, English sea captain William Phips (1651–1695) recovered the treasure from a Spanish ship that had sunk near Cuba in 1641. His divers used an air-filled barrel that was weighted so that it sank. However, the chances of recovering sunken treasure were slight until sonar and scuba equipment were invented. Scuba diving became popular after World World II (1939–1945). Amateur divers began to recover cannons and other finds from wrecks in the Mediterranean and off the Florida Keys. Marine archaeology developed at about the same time. Students aimed to preserve sunken ships and reconstruct their history rather than to locate treasure. Today, the search for shipwrecks relies on sophisticated underwater equipment, including cameras and robots. In 1985, this type of technology led to the discovery of the cruise liner HMS *Titanic*, which sank in the Atlantic in 1912.

*A pair of scuba divers explore remains in the sea in Truk, Micronesia. Micronesia comprises the westernmost islands of the Pacific Ocean.*

sponges, crustaceans, and shellfish from deep waters. During the 1870s, Forbes's theory was finally disproved by the historic voyage of the British research ship HMS *Challenger*. During its three-and-a-half-year voyage, *Challenger*'s scientists identified 4,000 new marine species, including many deep-sea creatures, and made important discoveries about the ocean floor.

### Submarines and sonar

According to legend, Macedonian king Alexander the Great (356–323 B.C.E.) had built the first crewed diving machine. This basic, barrel-shaped diving bell had a glass window for viewing sea life. The bell's only air supply was the bubble trapped at the top as the vessel was dropped into the water. British inventor John Holland built several primitive submarines during the 1870s, from which modern versions developed.

Submarines developed rapidly during World War I (1914–1918) when British and U.S. scientists developed sonar (SOH-NAHR; *SO*und *N*avigation *A*nd *R*anging). Sonar revolutionized marine exploration. The equipment includes an underwater sound source that sends pulses of sound waves toward the seabed, and a microphone that picks up the echoes that reflect

off the bottom and return to the surface. In shallow water, the echoes return quickly. In deep water, they return slowly. The depth of the water can be calculated by timing the echoes.

Submarines and research ships were soon using sonar to map the floors of the deep oceans. In 1925, the German research ship *Meteor* discovered the Mid-Atlantic Ridge, an undersea ridge that runs the length of the Atlantic, using the new equipment. Today, much of the work of mapping the ocean bottom is carried out by satellites orbiting Earth, which use microwaves rather than sound pulses.

In 1929, U.S. naturalist Charles W. Beebe (1877–1962) built a new kind of submersible (underwater vessel) capable of descending to great depths. It was a round diving chamber that resembled a large ball with portholes, and it could carry two people. Its round shape helped the craft to withstand the great pressure of the ocean depths. Beebe called his invention the bathysphere (BAH-thih-SFIR), from the Greek word *bathos*, which means "depth."

In 1930, Beebe and his partner Otis Barton took the craft on its first dive. The bathysphere was lowered by cables from a ship to a depth of 200 feet (60 m). By 1934, Beebe was descending

*The crewed research submersible* **Deepstar 4000** *can reach depths of 4,000 feet (1,219 m). It is shown here on the seabed off the coast of Mexico.*

Japanese bathyscaphe *Kaiko* explored the deepest part of the Mariana Trench—the Challenger Deep. It was equipped with five television cameras and mechanical arms for collecting heavy rock samples. Uncrewed submersibles are used by oil-prospecting companies and by television companies that make films of underwater life, as well as by ocean research institutes.

## Solutions from the oceans

Today the ocean depths are searched by gas and oil prospectors, drug companies, and researchers looking for solutions to problems on land. Mining companies use advanced drilling techniques and sonar to probe the seafloor for reserves of oil, natural gas, and valuable minerals. Rock samples from the ocean floor also help geologists to piece together the history of Earth.

Some scientists are looking to the seas to provide food. They are investigating the possibility of increasing fish catches by using sonar and chemical bait. As methods for removing salt from water improve, the oceans may also one day help to supply drinking water to parts of the world where water is scarce.

Drug companies collect samples of chemicals produced by some sea creatures to ward off underwater predators. These substances may one day help to develop cures for human viruses and diseases such as cancer. The oceans are also a source of abundant energy that may be tapped in the future. In addition, researchers investigate ways of harnessing the power of the waves and tides and even the heat energy of the oceans.

to record depths of 3,028 feet (908 m). In 1953, however, Swiss scientist August Piccard (1884–1962) smashed Beebe's record by reaching 10,000 feet (3,000 m) in a submersible he had designed called a bathyscaphe (BAH-thih-SKAF). In 1960, Piccard's son Jacques (1922–) and his partner Don Walsh made history by descending to the deepest point in the oceans, the Mariana Trench off the Philippines, in the bathyscaphe.

In 1964, U.S. scientist Allyn Vine built a submersible for a marine research institute called the Woods Hole Oceanographic Institution in Massachussetts. His craft, named *Alvin*, was modeled on Piccard's pioneering bathyscaphe but was fitted with underwater cameras and new instruments for measuring depth, salt levels, and water temperature, and with equipment for collecting samples of marine life.

The 1970s saw the development of self-contained atmospheric diving suits, or SCADS. These flexible metal suits allowed divers to walk on the seabed to depths of 2,000 feet (600 m). Early submersibles were connected to ships on the surface, but during the 1970s and 1980s, new, untethered craft were developed that could explore areas too small for a large ship.

Today's exploration of deep canyons in the ocean floor is carried out mostly by uncrewed submersibles. These small craft can maneuver in narrow canyons. Operated by remote control from the surface, they are also cheaper to run than piloted submersibles. In 1993, the unpiloted

### CHECK THESE OUT!
✔CONTINENTAL SHELF ✔GEYSER
✔OCEAN ✔OCEANOGRAPHY

# Mariner Probe

**A series of U.S. robot space probes sent to explore Venus, Mars, and Mercury**

The Mariner space probes were a series of automated missions launched by the National Aeronautics and Space Administration (NASA) in the 1960s and 1970s to explore the other planets in the inner Solar System (Mercury, Venus, and Mars). Mariner probes were the first spacecraft to successfully reach and send back data from these planets. This data transformed them from mysterious blurs in telescopes into actual worlds with their own unique features and histories.

The Mariner program began at the dawn of the Space Age. In 1958, just months after the first satellites were put into orbit, scientists at

*These technicians are preparing the spacecraft used in the* **Mariner 3** *and* **4** *missions to Mars.*

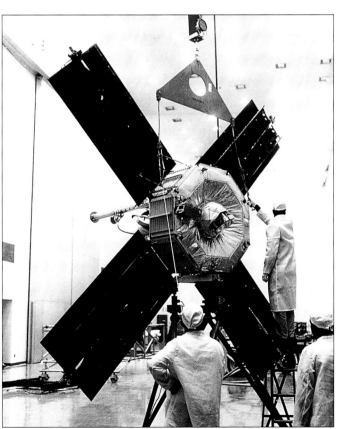

NASA's Jet Propulsion Laboratory (JPL) met to discuss possible missions to other planets. At this time, no spacecraft had even left low Earth orbit, a few hundred miles above Earth's surface. These scientists were trying to design a spacecraft that could survive space travel over millions of miles and then collect and send back scientific information from another planet. Considering how little experience they had, their design was a great success. With a few changes, it formed the basis for 10 different Mariner probes, seven of which were very successful.

## The Mariner design

Much of Mariner's success came from its simplicity. In the 1950s and early 1960s, NASA had access only to relatively small rockets. While they could carry reasonable payloads (cargoes) into orbit, the rockets did not have the power to launch heavy probes to the planets, so the early Mariners had to be kept very light. The first four missions had masses between 445 and 575 pounds (202 and 261 kg)—not very much for a spacecraft that must carry complex scientific instruments and be sturdy enough to withstand the shocks of launch and the risks of space flight.

The probes were built around the lightest, strongest materials available—the metals magnesium and aluminum. The body of the probe was a six- or eight-sided frame, with booms that could hold solar panels and steering jets and radio antennae (an-TEH-NEE; rods) sticking out of it. The Mariner probes could power themselves using solar energy because they were exploring the inner Solar System. They had panels of solar cells that folded out of the spacecraft once it was in flight and changed sunlight into electricity. A battery provided power for periods of darkness, such as during launch or when the Sun was eclipsed by a planet. Small rocket thrusters and a larger engine allowed the probe to change course during flight. Radio antennae received instructions from and sent information back to Earth.

## Instruments

The main body of the probe also had to contain most of the scientific instruments. These changed from mission to mission, although some experiments and pieces of equipment were standard. As the power of U.S. rockets improved, the later Mariner probes got bigger and could carry more instruments.

The payload (equipment needed for the mission) of an early Mariner mission, *Mariner 2* to Venus, included the following instruments:

**Cosmic dust collector**—a sounding board that detected the speed, momentum, and direction of impacts from dust particles in space.

**Solar plasma spectrometer**—an instrument that collected material from the solar wind streaming out from the Sun and measured the proportions of particles with different energy.

**Ion chamber**—a radiation detector to measure the amounts of high-energy radiation in interstellar space and around Venus.

**Microwave radiometer**—a set of antennae that detected radio waves emitted from below the Venusian cloud tops and compared them to radio waves from space. The strength of the radio waves from Venus allowed scientists to work out the planet's surface temperature.

**Infrared radiometer**—a companion to the microwave radiometer, designed to detect infrared (heat) radiation.

**Magnetometer**—a magnetic field detector built to detect any such field around the planet.

## Mariner missions

The early Mariner missions were put together in pairs, with duplicates of all the instruments on board each spacecraft. These were the early days of space exploration, and building pairs of probes meant there was always a backup if something went wrong with the first spacecraft. If both missions managed to reach their destination successfully, then the feedback was doubled.

The first pair of probes, *Mariners 1* and *2*, were aimed at exploring Venus, the closest planet to Earth. They were stripped-down versions of later probes, designed in a hurry because the Atlas-Centaur rocket that was being built to launch Mariner missions had fallen behind schedule, and NASA was desperate to beat the Soviet Union to Venus. (The Soviets had already made several failed attempts.) The tiny *Mariner 1*, weighing just 445 pounds (202 kg), was launched with a small Atlas-Agena rocket on July 22, 1962. The mission had to be aborted rapidly when the rocket went off course. On August 27, NASA tried

*This artwork shows the voyage of the* **Mariner 10** *probe to Venus (at center left) and Mercury (center right). The probe took pictures of Earth (upper left).*

## What did People Learn from Mariner?

**LOOK CLOSER**

The Mariner probes transformed people's views of the inner solar system. At Mercury, *Mariner 10* mapped nearly half the surface in 2,400 photographs, revealing a heavily cratered planet with almost no atmosphere and a temperature that varies between 760°F (405°C) in the daytime and –295°F (–185°C) at night.

For Venus, Mariner probes provided the first close-up images of the planet's cloud tops, measured the composition of the atmosphere, and discovered that the atmospheric pressure on the surface is 100 times that on Earth. *Mariner 2* showed that the surface temperature is at least 800°F (425°C) and discovered that Venus has only a very weak magnetic field.

At Mars, the Mariners transformed people's views twice. Before the first flybys, people still thought that the planet could harbor simple life-forms and surface water. The early Mariners destroyed this idea with their photographs of the barren southern half of the planet. *Mariner 9* then revealed a planet with a history more complex than astronomers had thought. The probes also showed that Mars had a very thin atmosphere and once had flowing water on its surface.

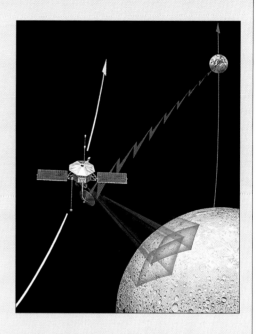

*Mariner 10 explores Mercury.*

again with *Mariner 2*, which successfully reached Earth's orbit and was then blasted on its way to Venus. During its trip, the probe sent back the first detailed information about interplanetary space and vital information about Venus itself.

*Mariners 3* and *4* were larger than the first missions, and they were aimed at Mars. *Mariner 3* was lost when part of the launch vehicle's nose cone did not fall away. This stopped the solar panels from unfolding and blocked the probe's navigation instruments. *Mariner 4* was delayed while the problems were resolved. It was launched successfully on November 28, 1964. It flew within 560 miles (900 km) of Mars in July 1965, sending back the first close-up pictures of the Martian surface. The *Mariner 5* probe was built as a backup for *Mariners 3* and *4*. After *Mariner 4*'s successful flyby (flight of a spacecraft past a body in space to collect data), it was modified for a flight to Venus in 1967.

By 1968, the Atlas-Centaur launcher was finally ready, so the next missions—*Mariners 6* and *7* to Mars—could be quite a bit heavier, at 908 pounds (413 kg). They could also carry more instruments, such as close-up and wide-angle television cameras and instruments to look at the

planet in light of different wavelengths. Both missions ran perfectly but flew past the planet's cratered southern regions, rather than the more interesting northern hemisphere of the planet.

*Mariner 9* was a more ambitious mission altogether. The spacecraft weighed over one ton and carried its own rocket engine, enabling it to slow down when it reached Mars and go into orbit around the planet. This was the first time anyone had tried to put a probe in orbit around another planet. It was a great success. Pictures from the mission revealed an exciting new side of Mars, with huge dormant (inactive) volcanoes, vast canyons, and ancient, dried-up riverbeds.

The final Mariner mission, *Mariner 10*, was designed to visit two planets. It flew by Venus and used the planet's gravity to swing it into a new orbit. It flew past Mercury not just once, but three times. The mission was a fantastic success, and *Mariner 10* is still the only space probe to have ever visited Mercury.

***CHECK THESE OUT!***

✔EXPLORER PROBE ✔MARS
✔MERCURY, PLANET ✔NASA ✔SPACE
✔VENUS ✔VIKING PROBE ✔VOYAGER PROBE

# Mars

Although today it is a dry, barren world with a thin atmosphere, astronomers and writers have long wondered whether there was once life on Mars. Space probes have shown that the planet once had a thicker atmosphere, a warmer climate, and water on its surface. These conditions might have given rise to simple life-forms.

*This global color view of Mars was processed from a number of images that were taken by the* **Viking Orbiter** *spacecraft.*

## Mars as a planet

Seen from Earth, the most obvious thing about Mars is its blood-red color. This is why Mars was named for the Roman god of war, and it has often been associated with aggression by astrologers. The planet orbits beyond Earth, and takes 1 year and 10½ months to move around the Sun. At its closest to Earth, Mars is just 35 million miles (56 million km) away. During these close approaches—called oppositions—astronomers can make out a lot of detail on the planet's surface. The most obvious features are white ice caps at the planet's north and south poles. There are also dark markings across the rest of the surface.

Mars is just over half the size of Earth. It has the lowest density of any of the rocky inner planets. This may be because it formed in a region of the Solar System where there was less heavy material for the young planet to pull in with its gravity.

## The Martian surface

Space probes have now mapped Mars in great detail and revealed a world with many contrasts. Only one of the ice caps is actually made up of water ice—the other is made of frozen carbon dioxide. Carbon dioxide is also the major gas in the planet's atmosphere, making up 95 percent of the total. The atmosphere itself is very thin—the air pressure on the surface is less than one percent of Earth's air pressure.

This thin atmosphere means that Mars is badly insulated, so temperature can change rapidly throughout a Martian day. Temperatures can approach freezing point at noon, and at night they can drop as low as –248°F (–120°C). When the overnight carbon dioxide frosts evaporate, they can sometimes form clouds and mists in the Martian atmosphere.

## HIGHLIGHTS

- Because of its blood-red color, Mars is named for the Roman god of war.

- Mars is just over half the size of Earth. Its surface is divided into two main regions: the cratered southern highlands and the flat northern plains.

- The Tharsis Rise (a huge bulge in the Martian surface) is home to the largest volcanoes in the Solar System, although they are now dormant.

- Mars has two moons—Phobos and Deimos—which are probably captured asteroids.

## LOOK CLOSER

# Martian Moons

Mars has two tiny moons: Phobos (pictured) and Deimos. Their names come from the Greek names for the god of war's companions— Fear and Panic. The moons were discovered in 1877 by U.S. astronomer Asaph Hall (1829–1907). They are some of the darkest objects in the Solar System.

The moons are just a few dozen miles wide and orbit close to the planet Mars. Phobos is so close that it orbits the planet in less than a day. Astronomers think this moon will be torn apart by Martian gravity by the year 2104.

Space probes have photographed both moons and have shown that they are lumpy, cratered objects. The best theory for their origin is that they are strays from the asteroid belt beyond Mars's orbit, captured by the planet's gravity.

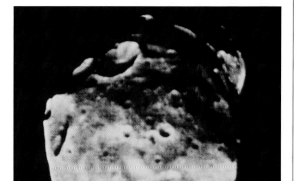

The Martian surface is divided into two areas with different features. The southern half of the planet is mostly raised highlands covered in craters, while the northern half is mostly wide open plains (the dark regions visible from Earth). The southern craters must have formed in the early days of the Solar System. Most of the impacts on Earth's Moon that took place at the same time as those on Mars happened more than 3.8 billion years ago, so the northern plains must have been formed or resurfaced after that.

The most impressive features on Mars are the huge volcanoes that occupy a large zone close to the equator on one side of the planet. The biggest of these, Olympus Mons, is 17 miles (27 km) above the average Martian surface. This is three times the size of Mount Everest. Three other volcanoes are positioned on top of the Tharsis Rise, a 2,500-mile (4,000-km) bulge in the Martian surface, roughly 6 miles (10 km) above the rest of the planet. The Martian volcanoes seem to be extinct today, but they may have been active as recently as 15 million years ago. Astronomers cannot be completely sure.

The Tharsis Rise is another mystery. It may have been pushed up by a hot spot in the Martian interior, or it may be a build-up of layers of lava (molten rock that has erupted above the surface). However it was caused, the Rise puts tremendous stress on the surrounding region of the planet.

As a result, a huge canyon system, called the Valles Marineris, has formed where the planet rifted (split) open to the south of the rise.

### Life on Mars?

The most fascinating features of the Martian surface are the dried-up riverbeds and floodplains that clearly show that the planet once had water running on its surface. Astronomers now think that the planet was much warmer in the distant past and that the water might still be locked away under the surface as ice.

If these astronomers are correct, Mars could have begun to evolve primitive life-forms. In 1996, a team of NASA scientists made headlines around the world. They analyzed a meteorite that had been blasted off the surface of Mars millions of years ago and fallen to Earth in Antarctica. They claimed that the meteorite, code-named ALH 84001, contains chemicals and perhaps even fossils that could have been caused by bacteria living on Mars more than 3 billion years ago. Their theory has caused disagreement among experts, and the arguments will continue until robot probes return conclusive rock samples from the planet itself.

***CHECK THESE OUT!***

✔EARTH ✔SOLAR SYSTEM ✔SPACE ✔VIKING PROBE ✔VOLCANO

# Mass

## The amount of matter that an object contains

Although mass is related to weight, the two are different. Weight is a measure of how much an object is attracted by gravity (which depends on the object's mass). The weight of an object changes from place to place according to the strength of the gravitational field. The mass of an object depends on the material from which the object is made, and it is always the same.

The strength of a planet's or a moon's gravitational field is proportional to its mass divided by the square of its radius. The weight of an object on the surface of the planet or moon is its mass multiplied by the gravitational field. The Moon's gravitational field is about one-sixth as strong as Earth's. Astronauts therefore weigh only one-sixth as much on the Moon and can float easily there. Their mass remains constant, but the change in gravity means they weigh less.

### Measuring mass

A massive object such as a boulder contains more matter than a leaf. Since weight at any place is proportional to mass, the mass of an object can be found by comparing its weight with that of another object of known mass. Scientists need to measure mass very precisely, so they use a standard measure of mass against which any other mass can be compared. This is a cylinder of platinum and iridium metals, whose mass is exactly 1 kg (2 pounds 3 ounces), kept at the International Bureau of Weights and Measures near Paris, France.

Mass can also be defined as the measure

*The standard measure of mass used by scientists today is this cylinder of platinum and iridium metals.*

of an object's inertia, or its resistance to acceleration. Inertia is the ratio of the total force on a body to the acceleration it produces. If this definition is used to measure a mass, then there must be a way of ensuring that the same force is applied to two different objects. A spring can be used to do this because the amount a spring stretches is proportional to the force it exerts.

A truck has more inertia than an automobile because it has more mass. If the truck and the automobile are traveling at the same speed, a much bigger force is needed to make the truck go twice as fast compared to the force needed to accelerate the car by the same amount. In other words, the force needed to accelerate an object increases with its mass.

### Changing mass to energy

When particles react with other particles, some of their mass can be changed into an equivalent amount of energy. This fact was discovered early in the 20th century by German-born U.S. physicist Albert Einstein (1879–1955). It is the principle behind the nuclear fusion reactions that power the Sun. At the Sun's core, hydrogen atoms combine to produce helium atoms. For every four hydrogen atoms, one helium atom is formed. However, the mass of a helium atom is a bit less than the mass of the four hydrogen atoms that were fused together. The difference in mass has been changed into heat and light energy.

***CHECK THESE OUT!***
✔GRAVITY ✔MATTER
✔RELATIVITY

# Matter

## All the material that makes up the Universe

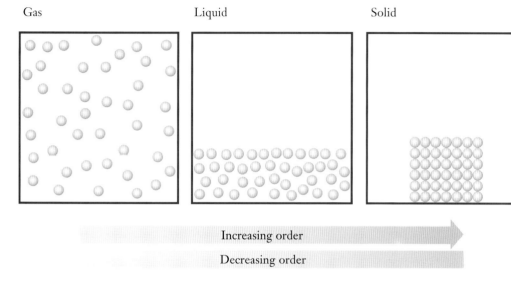

Gas       Liquid       Solid

Increasing order

Decreasing order

*Matter is not a single substance but a variety of different elements, each with different properties. A substance can be classed according to its state at room temperature: whether it is a solid, liquid, or gas. The particles of a gas are in a disordered state and move about freely, whereas in a solid the particles are packed tightly together.*

Everything in the Universe is made of matter, which is defined as anything that has mass and takes up space. Modern scientists understand what makes up matter and how it behaves, but there are many unanswered questions about where it came from and why it exists.

Matter may consist of an infinite (IN-fuh-nuht; endless) number of different substances, but all of these can be made from a relatively small number of chemical elements. Hydrogen is the most abundant element in the Universe—making up 75 percent of all matter. The smallest amount of an element is called an atom (A-tuhm), which, in turn, consists of smaller building blocks called protons, neutrons (NOO-trahnz), and electrons.

The different substances that make up matter have very different properties. For example, some are solid, some liquid, and some gases at room temperature. Each substance has different physical and chemical properties that distinguish it from other substances. The physical properties of a substance include its melting point (the temperature at which it changes from a solid to a liquid), how hard it is, and whether it conducts electricity. The chemical properties describe how the substance takes part in chemical reactions with other substances. For example, a property of iron is that it reacts with oxygen to make rust.

The idea of matter consisting of atoms is a very old one. It was proposed by the ancient Greek philosopher Democritus (around 468–370 B.C.E.), who believed that matter was made of tiny particles that could not be divided further. The word *atom* comes from the Greek word *atomos*, meaning "indivisible." Modern ideas about matter are based on the work of French chemists Antoine (1743–1794) and Marie (1758–1836) Lavoisier. The Lavoisiers discovered that, although substances change during chemical reactions, no matter ever appears or disappears. All the elements present in the chemicals at the start of the reaction (the reactants) can be found in the chemicals left at the end of the reaction (the products), usually in a different form. English chemist John Dalton (1766–1814) refined this theory by explaining how chemical reactions take place through the shuffling of the atoms present in the reactants.

Today, many astronomers believe that much of the matter in the Universe—perhaps 90 percent—exists in some form of "dark matter" that does not give out light. They speculate that it may be composed of exotic particles unlike those that make up ordinary atoms.

### *CHECK THESE OUT!*
✔MASS ✔UNIVERSE

# Mechanics

**The branch of physics that explains what happens when forces act on objects**

When scientists send rockets into space or satellites into orbit, they can work out what path the spacecraft must follow to end up in precisely the correct place. Considering the distance a spacecraft must travel, this is remarkable. That it is possible at all is due to a branch of physics called mechanics, which explains what happens to things when different forces act on them.

### Newton's laws

Mechanics can be traced back to the ideas of Greek philosopher Aristotle (384–322 B.C.E.), but it was English mathematician Sir Isaac Newton (1642–1727) who worked out the main principles of mechanics used by scientists today. Newton is best remembered for formulating the three laws that describe what happens to objects when forces act on them. Newton's laws of motion, as they are called, can be written down both in words and as simple mathematical

equations. It is these equations that rocket scientists feed into their computers to make sure that spacecraft successfully blast off into the correct orbits.

Newton's first law of motion says that an object will stay still (if it is not moving) or move along in a straight line at a steady speed (if it is already moving) unless some kind of force acts on it. This tendency of the object to keep on doing what it is already doing is called inertia (ih-NUHR-shuh). A car parked in the road will not just suddenly start moving all by itself. A car parked on a hill may start to roll downhill if the brake is not applied because the force of Earth's gravity acts on it. Similarly, a car moving along the highway at a steady speed will keep moving at that same speed unless the driver presses on the gas pedal. Newton's first law of motion explains what happens when there are no forces to disrupt the object.

The second law says that when a force acts

*This boy's body is working rather like a machine as he throws this ball. He is exerting a force on the ball in order to move it.*

452

*A car jack is a kind of lever. The force applied to push down one end of the lever is transferred to the opposite end, lifting the heavy weight.*

on an object, it makes the object accelerate (speed up) or decelerate (slow down). The bigger the force, the bigger the acceleration. The amount of acceleration also depends on the mass of the object; a bigger object will be accelerated less than a smaller object. If someone kicks a ball, the ball will speed up and fly through the air. The harder the ball is kicked, the faster it will fly. The heavier the ball, the more difficult it becomes to kick it into the air.

Newton's first two laws of motion do not offer any particularly surprising information: still objects stay still, moving objects keep moving, and balls fly into the air when they are kicked. Newton's third law is more challenging. The third law says that when a force acts on an object, it produces another force called a reaction. The reaction is the same size as the original force (which is sometimes called the action) but pushes in the opposite direction. Newton's third law explains why skateboarders shoot forward when they kick back against the sidewalk. The backward-kicking action causes a reaction force that pushes the skateboard forward. The same idea is also used in a jet engine, where hot exhaust gas rushing backward pushes an airplane forward through the sky.

## How machines do work

In everyday life machines are thought of as large and noisy automated (operating automatically) mechanical or electronic devices, such as the robots in a car-building plant. Scientists think of machines in a more precise way. In physics, a machine is any device that transmits a force or changes its size or direction. Wheelbarrows, spades, and sugar tongs are thought of as machines by physicists.

A machine does work. It makes a force act over a distance. A jack that lifts a car up into the

air does work against the force of gravity pulling downward. The amount of work is equal to the force (the weight of the car) multiplied by the distance over which it acts (the height the car rises up in the air). Energy is needed to do work, so someone has to operate the jack. This energy is not lost. It is changed into a type of stored energy, called potential energy, which can be released later. The rate at which a machine does

---

# EVERYDAY SCIENCE

## Aristotle's Ideas about Mechanics

Greek philosopher Aristotle (384–322 B.C.E.) pondered the principles of mechanics long before Sir Isaac Newton. Unlike modern scientists, Aristotle believed that matter was made from the four elements: air, fire, water, and earth. His laws of motion were also very different from Newton's. He believed that air and fire moved upward, while water and Earth moved downward. Objects could move through the air because the air opened up before them and pinched closed behind them.

Although some of Aristotle's ideas seem strange now, his approach to science, based on careful thinking and reasoning, is recognized as important today. Unlike Aristotle, however, modern scientists would not accept a theory as true until it has been tested many times by experiment.

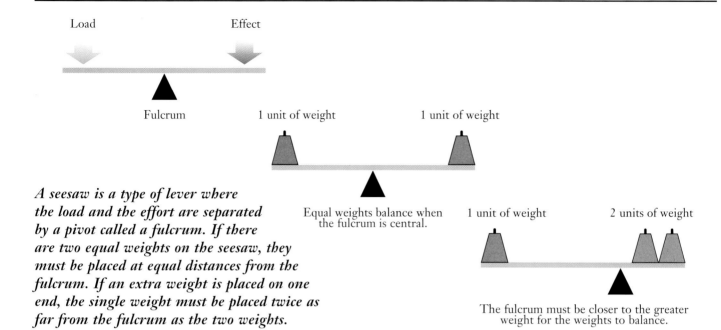

*A seesaw is a type of lever where the load and the effort are separated by a pivot called a fulcrum. If there are two equal weights on the seesaw, they must be placed at equal distances from the fulcrum. If an extra weight is placed on one end, the single weight must be placed twice as far from the fulcrum as the two weights.*

Load

Effect

Fulcrum

1 unit of weight

1 unit of weight

Equal weights balance when the fulcrum is central.

1 unit of weight

2 units of weight

The fulcrum must be closer to the greater weight for the weights to balance.

work (and uses energy) is called its power. The more work that a machine does in a certain amount of time, the greater its power.

The main purpose of a machine is to make a job easier for people. For example, it might reduce the amount of force that needs to be used. A wheelbarrow makes it possible to move a heavy load from one place to another, substituting a very small force of rolling friction for a much larger force of sliding friction to be overcome.

## EVERYDAY SCIENCE

### The Bicycle

In a bicycle, several different kinds of machines are joined together. A bicycle is freewheeling, which means the wheels can carry its passenger along even without pedal power. The handlebars are levers: to an extent, the longer they are, the easier it is to steer. The pedals are also levers. Because there are two of them, each one has to be pushed down only half the time.

Bicycles also rely on a gear chain that drives the gears on the back wheel from those attached to the pedals. Selecting different gears makes it easier to ride quickly on a straight road or to cycle uphill. Cars and motorcycles also use gears, but they are hidden away beneath the engine. All of these machines within a machine make the bicycle a very efficient form of transportation.

A machine can also reduce the force needed to do a job. Instead of a person having to pick up an entire load and carry it, they have only to lift one end of the barrow and push it. In this case, the barrow is working as a kind of machine called a lever.

### Types of machines

Levers are probably the oldest machines in existence. In its most familiar form, a lever is just like a seesaw. It has a load at one end, a pivot point in the middle called a fulcrum, and a place at the other end where a force called the effort is applied. If two people of the same weight sit on a seesaw and the fulcrum is placed exactly in the middle, the seesaw will work properly. If two people sit at one end, they can still be lifted into the air, but only if they sit much nearer to the fulcrum than the person at the other end. Near to the fulcrum, a greater amount of human force is needed to work the lever.

Most levers work by increasing the force that can be applied to something by increasing the distance between the effort and the fulcrum. For example, a long wrench is easier to turn than a short one. Levers are sometimes called force multipliers. Everyday levers include crowbars, car jacks, and wheelbarrows.

A ramp (sometimes called an inclined plane) is a machine that makes it easier to lift heavy objects. It is much easier to push something heavy up a ramp than it is to lift it. A screw is also a machine. It works just like a ramp wrapped around itself into a spiral. A machine called an auger (AW-guhr) uses a rotating screw to lift earth from the ground. A similar, simple machine called an Archimedes's screw (named for the Greek philosopher) has been used to lift water since ancient times. The screw is built at an angle so that the water can pour into a channel.

Pulleys are also useful machines. They consist of one or more wheels and ropes arranged in such a way as to reduce the force (effort) needed to lift a heavy object. The more ropes and wheels that are used, the less the effort needed. If two ropes are used, the effort needed is reduced by half. However, the rope must be pulled twice as far. A pulley with two ropes is said to have a mechanical advantage of two.

*A pulley with two ropes helps a person to lift double the weight with the same amount of effort, but he or she must pull the rope twice as far.*

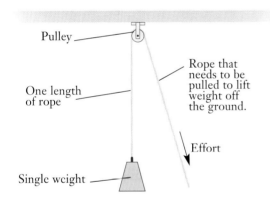

Pulley

One length of rope

Rope that needs to be pulled to lift weight off the ground.

Effort

Single weight

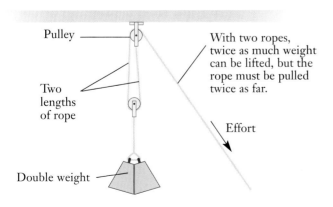

Pulley

Two lengths of rope

With two ropes, twice as much weight can be lifted, but the rope must be pulled twice as far.

Effort

Double weight

### Rotational motion

Newton's laws are most often used to understand what happens to objects moving in straight lines. The laws can also be used for rotational motion (what happens when objects move in circles).

Newton's first law says that an object will move in a straight line unless a force acts on it. This means that an object moving around in a circle, such as a satellite orbiting Earth, is constantly acted on by some force. A centripetal force is always present when an object follows a circular path. Acting from the object in toward the center of the circle, a centripetal force constantly tugs the object inward. With a satellite, the centripetal force is Earth's gravity. When a person spins a stone tied to a piece of string, the centripetal force comes from the tension in the string. If the string breaks, the stone flies off in a straight line—just as Newton's first law says—because there is no longer a centripetal force to keep it moving in a circle.

### *CHECK THESE OUT!*
✔FORCE ✔GRAVITY ✔MOMENTUM ✔MOTION

# Mediterranean Sea

**An intercontinental sea bordered by Europe, North Africa, and the Middle East**

The Mediterranean is the largest inland sea in the world, with an area of 1.1 million square miles (3 million sq km). From west to east, it stretches 2,330 miles (3,750 km), with a north–south distance of 500 miles (800 km). Its deepest point is 16,000 feet (5,090 m).

The Mediterranean Sea is almost entirely landlocked (enclosed by land). It lies between Europe, Asia, and Africa. The narrow Straits of Gibraltar link it to the Atlantic Ocean, and the Sea of Marmara connects it to the Black Sea.

The Mediterranean is made up of a number of smaller seas, partly separated by peninsulas (narrow portions of land extending out into the water) and islands. These include the Tyrrhenian Sea between Italy and Sardinia.

## Climate and currents

The Mediterranean region experiences long, hot summers and mild, wet winters. Evaporation from the sea is high. In summer, so much water

*A satellite image showing the Mediterranean Sea. The Sea joins the Atlantic Ocean in the west (left).*

is lost that salt levels rise in the remaining water. In winter, this salty water cools, sinks, and flows out into the Atlantic Ocean. It is replaced by less salty water flowing in near the surface.

The fresher water entering from the Atlantic flows mainly southward along the North African coast. Generally, the surface waters of the Mediterranean flow counterclockwise. There are many wind systems, including the hot, dusty sirocco that blows from the Sahara Desert.

Tides in the Mediterranean are weak, with a range of less than 3 feet (1 m) between high and low tide marks. The sea surface is warm in summer, rising to 86°F (30°C) off the coast of Libya. In winter, surface temperatures fall to 41°F (5°C) in the Adriatic.

The Mediterranean contains a range of marine plants and animals. These include commercially valuable species such as tuna and shellfish.

## Ancient history of the Mediterranean

In ancient times, dating from the Paleozoic era, most of the Mediterranean was part of an ocean called the Tethys. Later, movements of the giant tectonic plates that make up Earth's crust drained much of this body of water. Earthquakes and volcanoes often occur along the boundaries between tectonic plates. Several parts of the Mediterranean still experience earthquakes and volcanic eruptions, notably Turkey and Greece.

## The sea floor

An undersea ridge divides the floor of the Mediterranean into western and eastern basins, which in turn are divided into smaller basins by lesser ridges. Deposits of oil and natural gas lie in the rocks of the seabed. Gas has been discovered in the Adriatic, and oil has been found off Spain.

### CHECK THESE OUT!
✔ATLANTIC OCEAN ✔INLAND SEA
✔ISLAND ✔PLATE TECTONICS

# Melting and Boiling Points

## The temperatures at which substances change from solid to liquid and from liquid to gas

*This digital thermometer shows ice melting at 0°C.*

Water can exist in three different states: solid ice, liquid water, and steam, a gas. The state in which it is found depends on the temperature and pressure of the water. Given the right combination of temperature and pressure, any substance can be a solid, liquid, or gas. Substances do not change states gradually, like the way iron rusts, but in a sudden jump. The point of change from a solid to a liquid is the melting point of a substance. The point of change from a liquid to a gas is the boiling point.

If a beaker is filled with crushed ice, a thermometer is placed inside it, and the contents are heated up with a bunsen burner, water's behavior when changing from solid through liquid to gas can be easily observed. The temperature of the ice rises regularly until it reaches its melting point of 32°F (0°C). At this point, even though more heat is added, the temperature stays constant. Once all the ice has become liquid water, the temperature begins to rise again until the water reaches its boiling point of 212°F (100°C). Once again, the temperature stays constant until all the water has turned to steam. If the steam is trapped in some kind of a closed tank, its temperature begins to rise again when all the liquid has vaporized (turned to gas).

Why does this happen? Atoms (the building blocks of chemical elements) in solids are packed tightly together, like cars in a full parking lot. Forces of attraction between them keep them in place. Atoms in a liquid are more widely spaced and can move around to a certain extent, like boats in a harbor. They still exert forces of attraction on one another, but these are much weaker than in a solid. To turn a solid into a liquid, energy must be added to overcome the forces and push the atoms apart. When ice is heated in a beaker, the temperature stops rising at the melting point because all the energy from the burner is being used to push the atoms apart and change the solid into a liquid.

Atoms in a gas are more widely spaced than those in a liquid. They move about freely like airplanes in the sky. Changing a liquid into a gas means pushing the atoms even farther apart, which uses energy. As water boils into steam, all the energy from the burner is used to turn the liquid into gas, so the temperature stops rising.

### CHECK THESE OUT!
✔EVAPORATION ✔GAS ✔LIQUID
✔SOLID ✔TEMPERATURE

# Mercury, Metal

## A bright, shiny metal that is liquid at normal temperatures

The only metal that is liquid at normal temperatures is mercury. Mercury does not solidify until it is cooled to –38°F (–38.9°C). It also has a very low boiling point, at 673.8°F (356.7°C). This temperature range makes it an ideal fluid for use in several types of thermometers.

Some metallic mercury emerges from rocks as silvery drops, but it appears more commonly as a bright red sulfide called vermilion. The ancient Egyptians were probably the first to discover mercury, and it was certainly known by the Romans. The principal sources in Europe are in Tuscany, Italy, and Spain. The Romans called it *hydrargyrum*, which means "liquid silver" and gives mercury its chemical symbol—Hg. The metal got its modern name in the Middle Ages, when alchemists connected each of the seven known metals with the seven known planets. However, mercury is still often called quicksilver.

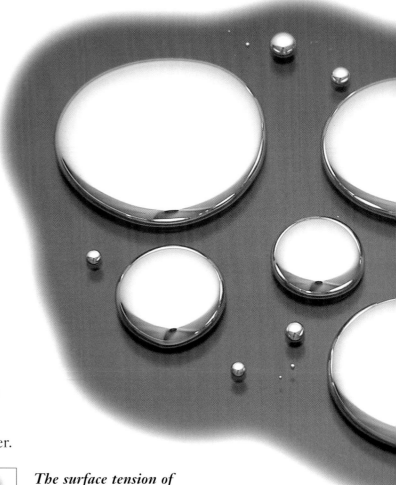

*The surface tension of mercury is so high that the smaller droplets form almost perfect spheres.*

## HIGHLIGHTS

◆ Mercury is the only metal that is liquid at normal temperatures.

◆ Mercury is chemically related to zinc and cadmium.

◆ The liquid metal is not poisonous to the human body. However, compounds of mercury and its vapor are extremely poisonous.

◆ Mercury is not as good a conductor of electricity as some other metals, but it is useful in electrical instruments because it is not affected by air.

◆ Mercury can be used to dissolve other metals. The solutions that are made are called amalgams.

### Physical and chemical properties

Mercury has a high density. This makes it useful in barometers, as a short column (30 inches or 76 cm) provides a pressure of one atmosphere. It is not as good a conductor of heat and electricity as many other metals. However, mercury is not affected by air at normal temperatures, and for this reason it is often used in electrical control and measuring instruments.

Mercury is related to the elements above it in the periodic table—zinc and cadmium. Unlike them, however, it can form compounds in both +1 and +2 oxidation states.

Despite a number of scares in recent years, the liquid metal itself is not poisonous to the human body. Its vapor, on the other hand, is extremely poisonous. Compounds of mercury are also highly poisonous. However, most of these compounds are only slightly soluble in body fluids and have been used in medicine for centuries. Mercurous chloride, called calomel (KA-luh-muhl), was used to treat syphilis (SIH-fuh-luhs; an infectious disease) before antibiotics were developed.

If mercury is heated gently in air, it gradually forms a crust of oxide. When this oxide is heated to a higher temperature, it decomposes (breaks down) again into the metal and oxygen. This was how English chemist Joseph Priestly (1733–1804) discovered the element oxygen in 1774.

## Industrial production

The principal ore of mercury is the sulfide cinnabar. This ore occurs in areas where volcanic activity is relatively recent, and it is sometimes associated with hot springs. More than half the world's supply of cinnabar is found in Italy and Spain. It also occurs in the Coastal Range of California. The traditional method of extracting the metal from cinnabar was to roast it in a blast furnace. This process produced sulfur dioxide and mercury vapor, which was then condensed. Because the vapor is highly poisonous, and the sulfur dioxide polluted the atmosphere, safer methods have now been developed. The cinnabar is dissolved in other chemicals, and the metal is recovered by electrolysis (the use of an electrical current to split a compound into its elements) or by adding zinc or aluminum.

## Practical uses

An unusual property of mercury is its ability to dissolve other metals—even gold. The solutions it forms are called amalgams. For many years, dentists have used an amalgam of silver and

## EVERYDAY SCIENCE

### Mercury Poisoning

Acute mercury poisoning is usually due to the accidental swallowing of mercury compounds. It can also result from a few other situations. There is a danger that the vapor from a broken thermometer, spilled on a carpet, may produce symptoms of mercury poisoning, particularly among young children. If swallowed, mercury enters the kidneys, where it causes a buildup of toxic substances in the blood. Such a buildup ultimately leads to death.

Chronic mercury poisoning results from exposure to mercury vapors or mercury compounds. During the 19th century, mercuric nitrate was used in the treatment of felt for hats. In Danbury, Connecticut, many workers in the hat-making industry became known as mad hatters. Their exposure to the poisonous mercuric nitrate resulted in a strange jerking walk, stammering, and even loss of teeth.

In the early 1950s, there was an outbreak of mercury poisoning in the Japanese town of Minamata. Symptoms suffered by the townspeople included weakening of the muscles, loss of vision, and paralysis. Some citizens even died. The poisoning was traced to mercury-containing waste from a local factory.

mercury to fill tooth cavities. However, fears about the poisonous nature of mercury have led to the use of other materials.

Mercury vapor is used in both street and stadium lighting. The vapor has also been used instead of steam in some power plants.

Until recently, organic (carbon- and hydrogen-containing) mercury compounds were widely used as fungicides (substances for killing fungi) and pesticides (chemicals for killing insects and weeds). However, scientists discovered a buildup of mercury in fish such as tuna and salmon. As a result, the use of mercury fungicides and pesticides, and the discharge of industrial wastes containing mercury, has been prohibited in the United States since the early 1970s.

***CHECK THESE OUT!***
✔AIR PRESSURE ✔ALLOY ✔CAPILLARY ACTION ✔METAL

# Mercury, Planet

**The closest planet to the Sun, and the hottest planet in the Solar System**

The hottest planet in the Solar System is Mercury, which is also the smallest planet after Pluto. Mercury is relatively close to Earth (at closest approach it is 58 million miles or 92 million km away), yet it has only been visited by one space probe so far.

## Mercury as a planet

Mercury was named for the winged messenger of the gods in Roman mythology because of the speed at which the planet moves across the sky. It is only 35 million miles (57 million km) from the Sun, and takes 88 days to orbit the Sun. It is therefore always very close to the Sun as seen from Earth. It can only be spotted close to the horizon before sunrise or after sunset. Along with its small size, these difficult viewing conditions meant that very little was known about Mercury before the Space Age.

Mercury is a terrestrial (Earthlike) planet. Like Venus and Mars, as well as Earth, it is made up of rock and iron. Mercury measures just 1,514 miles (2,439 km) across and has $\frac{1}{18}$ of the mass of Earth. Throughout a typical day, the temperature on Mercury changes from up to 760°F (405°C) to less than –295°F (–185°C).

The planet's rotation is also mysterious. At first astronomers thought that it spun once in each orbit, with one face permanently turned to the Sun, in the same way that the Moon keeps one face turned to Earth. However, astronomers today know that Mercury's day is equal to 59 Earth days and is exactly two-thirds the length of its year. For this reason, Mercury rotates three times for every two orbits of the Sun.

*This photomosaic of the Borealis Region of Mercury was made up of several images from space probe* **Mariner 10.**

## The composition of Mercury

Mercury has almost no atmosphere. The planet's gravity is barely strong enough to hold on to molecules of gas. The heat from the Sun also heats up the few molecules that are there until they mostly fly off into space.

Mercury's surface is covered in lightweight silicate (sandy) rocks, similar to those found on Earth. Astronomers think its interior is very different from those of the other terrestrial planets because Mercury is the densest planet in the Solar System. It has a much greater mass than they would expect for its size. If Earth and Mercury were made of the same materials, Earth would be denser (its greater gravity would make the planet more compressed). Mercury is, however, denser than Earth, so the interior of the planet must contain huge amounts of heavy metals—most probably iron and nickel. The interiors of all the terrestrial planets divide into three zones: an outer solid crust, an inner mantle, and a central metal core. Earth's core is made of molten metal and occupies about 54 percent of the planet's radius. Mercury's core may extend to up to 70 percent of the planet's radius, with only a thin mantle between the core and the crust.

## Surface features

Mercury's surface is covered with craters. The planet has no air or water to cause erosion and was never large enough to develop volcanoes or shifting surface plates that could recreate the surface over time. The only changes that have happened since the planet's formation have been caused by meteorite impacts from space and from the action of gravity leveling the surface.

The result is a planet covered in craters, like Earth's own Moon. As there is no atmosphere, even the smallest particles from space manage to reach the surface, creating microcraters and slowly turning the surface into dust. Scientists know from lunar rock samples that most meteorite bombardment happened in the early days of the Solar System (up to about 3.8 billion years ago). Few craters have formed since, so Mercury's surface must be at least this old.

Apart from its craters, Mercury's surface is dominated by long ridges (scarps), often over 1.5 miles (2.5 km) high. These seem to be faults

### LOOK CLOSER

## Mercury's Core

There are various theories about why Mercury has such a large core for its size. One idea is that the planet was involved in a major collision as it was forming. This could have knocked away a large chunk of Mercury's mantle and crust and melted the remainder so that the planet reformed around its core, with a reduced outer layer. This might also explain why Mercury's orbit is eccentric (unusual) and tilted at an angle to most of the other planets.

Another idea is that as Mercury formed, the Sun's heat caused the lighter elements to boil away and not condense around the core. It is also possible that the light elements behaved exactly like the gases in Mercury's atmosphere today. They were too hot and moved too quickly to be captured by the planet's weak gravity.

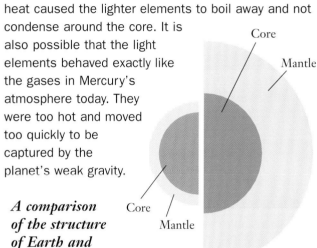

*A comparison of the structure of Earth and Mercury.*

Core
Mantle
Core
Mantle
**Mercury**  **Earth**

between different sections of the crust. These faults may have been formed by tides, as the Sun's powerful gravity tugged at the soft surface of the young planet—in the same way that it pulls today on Earth's oceans.

The single most striking feature on Mercury is the Caloris Basin, the remains of a huge meteorite impact early in the planet's history. The floor is 5.5 miles (9 km) deep, and the basin is surrounded by ripples across the surrounding plains. It seems that the impact was large enough to send shock waves right around the planet—on the exact opposite side is a jumbled region called the weird terrain, where the shock waves met up again and created chaos.

### CHECK THESE OUT!
✔CRATER ✔MILKY WAY ✔SPACE ✔UNIVERSE

# Mercury Mission

## The first U.S. crewed flights into space, launched between 1961 and 1963

A s soon as the United States had launched its first successful satellites in early 1958, the newly formed National Aeronautics and Space Administration (NASA) began making plans for putting humans into space and returning them safely to Earth. However, NASA was lagging behind the Soviet Union in the space race, mainly because their rockets were less powerful than Soviet launch vehicles. To catch up, the Mercury project was developed from existing technologies rather than built from scratch. This meant rockets already in use were modified, so the size of the Mercury spacecraft had to be kept to a minimum. Therefore, the Mercury missions could carry only one astronaut—a crew of two or more would have been too heavy for the launch vehicle to take into orbit.

### Selecting astronauts

The U.S. president of the time, Dwight D. Eisenhower, ordered that the first U.S. astronauts should be recruited from the

*The* Mercury-Atlas 7, *carrying astronaut M. Scott Carpenter, was successfully launched from Cape Canaveral, Florida, on May 24, 1962. Carpenter became the second American to orbit Earth.*

## HIGHLIGHTS

♦ The Mercury missions were one-person flights. The first spacecraft did not even reach orbit, but the last remained in space for over 30 hours.

♦ The seven chosen Mercury astronauts had to go through a tough selection procedure.

♦ The first U.S. citizen in space was Alan B. Shepard, on May 5, 1961.

♦ The first U.S. citizen in orbit was John Glenn, on February 20, 1962.

military. At the time, the United States was locked in a Cold War with the Soviet Union, and space was an important battlefield in the public relations war. It was felt that military pilots were right to do the job and to send out a powerful message about U.S. heroism.

One advantage of military pilots was that details of their health, mental state, and flying skills were already on record. This made the selection process much easier. Once the basic requirements for a Mercury astronaut had been worked out, a review board checked the records of 508 military fliers and selected 110 men for interview.

After interviewing the first 69 candidates, NASA realized they had a problem—the organization was flooded with suitable candidates. As a result, the last batch of pilots were not even interviewed, and the examination program was toughened up. The organizers knew that no one would drop out of the program willingly, so they selected only the top 6 candidates, rather than the top 12, for full training.

Of the 69 candidates, 6 were too tall to fit inside a Mercury spacecraft and 27 were eliminated through severe physical and mental testing. This left 36 to go on to an even tougher second round of physical tests, involving a full medical examination, a thorough set of X rays, heart tests, and many others.

Only one candidate failed the medical. The other 35 were tested further at the Aerospace Medical Laboratory in Dayton, Ohio. Potential astronauts had their physical and mental strength tested to the limit. Acceleration and pressure suit trials tested their ability to cope with the enormous forces, many times the strength of gravity, that they would encounter in the flight. Other trials investigated how well the

---

## EVERYDAY SCIENCE

### Women Astronauts?

In the early stages of planning for Mercury, NASA came very close to selecting female astronauts for its test program. The agency's chief medical adviser, Randolph Lovelace II, pointed out that because women generally weighed less, they would be ideal astronauts for the underpowered rockets of the time.

Lovelace called in 25 top U.S. female pilots to take part in secret tests and 13 of them passed as suitable for astronaut training. Most of them scored higher in the tests than the final Mercury Seven. The tests also showed that female astronauts had other advantages. They required smaller oxygen supplies and coped better with the isolation of space travel. However, unfortunately for the selected women, the male-dominated society of the time got in their way. When NASA headquarters learned about Lovelace's tests, they forced the introduction of new regulations for astronaut selection. All candidates had to have experience flying military jets, and the U.S. military did not allow women to pilot jets at that time.

---

astronauts could cope with heat, noise, isolation, and cramped environments. There were also intelligence tests.

### The Mercury Seven

Finally, NASA had 18 suitable candidates. The selection board could not agree on just six to become astronauts, so they picked seven and asked the others to reapply for later programs. The Mercury Seven were (in order of their flights): Alan B. Shepard, Virgil Grissom, John Glenn, Malcolm Scott Carpenter, Walter Schirra, L. Gordon Cooper, and Donald K. Slayton.

The astronaut trainees became national heroes before they had even gone into space. Only six flew on Mercury missions. Slayton, who was to have flown on *Mercury 4*, was grounded when medics discovered he had an irregular heartbeat. He became head of NASA's newly formed astronaut office and continued to argue that he was fit to go into space. He eventually made it in 1975, on board the joint U.S.–Soviet Apollo–Soyuz mission.

## Designing the spacecraft

Meanwhile, the Mercury spacecraft was being built. NASA had asked various companies to produce designs in 1959, and the winner came from the McDonnell Aircraft Corporation. At the time, NASA had only two launch vehicles—the small Redstone rocket and the larger, newer, and less reliable Atlas rocket. Mercury was designed to attach to either vehicle so that test flights could begin with a Redstone while Atlas was being perfected.

The spacecraft was a tiny, cone-shaped vehicle, 9 feet (2.7 m) high and 6 feet (1.8 m) across. It was made of the lightweight metal titanium (ty-TAY-nee-uhm) and a nickel alloy. The astronaut squeezed through a hatch cut in the side, onto a seat facing a panel of controls and instruments. Originally, the capsule had just two tiny portholes, replaced on later flights by a larger rectangular window. The astronaut had to wear a full spacesuit with helmet, just in case the spacecraft's oxygen supply failed.

*Astronaut Virgil Ivan "Gus" Grissom prepares for the launch of* Liberty Bell 7, *the second and final suborbital flight launched aboard a Redstone rocket.*

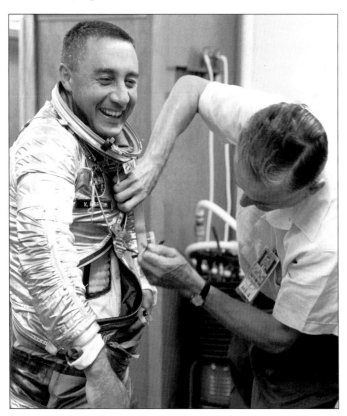

There were 18 small thrusters dotted around the outside of the capsule. These devices could be fired in different combinations to change the spacecraft's orientation (OHR-ee-uhn-TAY-shuhn; direction). At the bottom end of the cone were three retrorockets, designed to slow down the spacecraft in its orbit and drop it back toward Earth at the end of the mission. Once these rockets had carried out their job, they fell away to expose the base of the cone, which was heavily shielded against the heat with layers of fiberglass and plastic.

As the Mercury capsule fell back to Earth, friction with the atmosphere heated the bottom of the spacecraft to around 3000°F (1650°C). The heat shield was designed to slowly burn away into space, carrying the heat with it and keeping the internal temperature low.

Above the cone was a cylinder containing the main and reserve parachutes. Once safely back inside the atmosphere, the parachutes would open out to slow down the capsule, before gently dropping it into the sea.

When attached to a rocket and ready for launch, the entire capsule was capped by a 21-foot (6.3-m) escape tower (an open framework with three rocket motors at the top). In the event of a problem during launch, these motors were designed to fire and carry the capsule safely out of the way.

## Into orbit

The Mercury launch vehicle and rockets had to undergo rigorous testing before NASA was ready to risk a crewed launch. An important milestone came in January 1961 when a chimpanzee astronaut called Ham survived a flight into space and returned safely to Earth. The Redstone rocket was powerful enough to put a capsule into space, though not into orbit.

Eventually the go-ahead was given for Alan Shepard to launch on May 5, 1961—less than a month after Soviet cosmonaut Yuri Gagarin had become the first person in space. Shepard's flight lasted just 15 minutes, reaching an altitude of 115 miles (185 km) before his capsule *Freedom 7* splashed down in the Atlantic Ocean.

Following Shepard's pioneering flight, NASA launched one more suborbital (not completing an

## LOOK CLOSER

# The Mercury Flights in Detail

**Friendship 7**: *February 20, 1962*
Duration: 4 hours, 56 minutes (3 orbits)
Astronaut: John H. Glenn (pictured left)
The first orbital Mercury flight, launched by an Atlas rocket. Mission engineers were worried that the capsule's heat shield might have come loose, so Glenn did not release the retrorockets. They stayed attached as an extra heat shield.

**Aurora 7**: *May 24, 1962*
Duration: 4 hours, 56 minutes (3 orbits)
Astronaut: M. Scott Carpenter
A near-perfect flight, but problems during reentry meant the spacecraft splashed down 250 miles (400 km) off target in the Atlantic. The recovery team took three hours to locate and retrieve the capsule.

**Sigma 7**: *October 3, 1962*
Duration: 9 hours, 14 minutes (6 orbits)
Astronaut: Walter M. Schirra Jr.
An extended mission that was perfectly performed and gave NASA the confidence for longer spaceflights. The capsule splashed down in the Pacific Ocean within sight of the recovery fleet.

**Freedom 7**: *May 5, 1961*
Duration: 15 minutes, 25 seconds
Astronaut: Alan B. Shepard
The first suborbital Mercury flight.

**Liberty Bell 7**: *July 21, 1961*
Duration: 15 minutes, 37 seconds
Astronaut: Virgil Ivan "Gus" Grissom
Second suborbital flight. After splashdown, the spacecraft's hatch blew accidentally and the capsule started to flood. Grissom was forced to abandon the capsule and had to be rescued by helicopter as his spacesuit became waterlogged.

**Faith 7**: *May 15, 1963*
Duration: 34 hours, 20 minutes (22 orbits)
Astronaut: L. Gordon Cooper
The last and longest Mercury flight, designed to test how astronauts functioned during long periods in zero gravity. Cooper coped with several equipment failures during the flight and made a manual reentry to land within 1 mile (1.6 km) of the recovery ship USS *Kearsage*. L. Gordon Cooper was the last U.S. citizen to fly alone in space.

orbit) flight and a number of other tests before they were satisfied with the safety of the Atlas rocket. On February 20, 1962, astronaut John Glenn became the first U.S. citizen in orbit, with a flight that lasted five hours.

Three more orbital Mercury flights followed, making a total of six, each a little longer than the previous one, until the final Mercury mission made 22 orbits around Earth. By this time,

around May 1963, the Gemini program—the next step toward the goal of a mission to the Moon—was underway and the Mercury mission was brought to an end.

***CHECK THESE OUT!***
✔APOLLO MISSION ✔EXPLORER PROBE
✔MARINER PROBE ✔MARS ✔MOON ✔NASA
✔SPACE ✔VENUS ✔VIKING PROBE ✔VOYAGER PROBE

# Mesozoic Era

**The part of geological time that lasted from 245 to 66.4 million years ago**

Geological time is divided up by geologists (scientists who study the structure and history of rocks) into sections called eras and periods. This has been done by studying the strata (STRAH-tuh; rock layers) and their fossils (preserved evidence of past life). The fossils in the rocks and the rock sequence allow scientists to work out a relative timescale. Eras are large sections of time that are divided into smaller parts called periods. Because fossils of dinosaurs and reptiles are found in the Mesozoic (MEH-zuh-ZOH-ik) rocks, this part of the time scale is often called the age of reptiles. The word *Mesozoic* means "middle life" and the era is the middle of the three main eras of time. Before it came the Paleozoic era (ancient life) and after it the Cenozoic era (recent life). The Mesozoic era lasted just under 180 million years, ending 66.4 million years ago.

*Maiasaura were herbivorous (grass- and plant-eating) duck-billed dinosaurs that lived in the Mesozoic era.*

## HIGHLIGHTS

◆ The Mesozoic era is divided into three periods: the Triassic, the Jurassic, and the Cretaceous.

◆ In the oceans during the era, the ammonites flourished along with many other creatures.

◆ Toward the end of the era, in the Cretaceous period, the Atlantic Ocean began to form as South America and Africa split apart.

◆ At the end of the era, over a quarter of all the plant and animal groups died out.

The rocks of each era contain fossils showing the evolution (process of change) of certain living organisms. Toward the end of an era, there is evidence in the strata of a widespread extinction (dying out) of organisms. In the Paleozoic era primitive reptiles evolved. At the end of the era, the trilobites (TRY-luh-BYTS), which had lived in the oceans for tens of millions of years, died out.

## The fossils in the rocks

Geologists use fossils to mark places on the time scale. The coiled shells of fossil ammonites (A-muh-NYTS; ancient sea creatures) are used to date the rock of Mesozoic rocks. Ammonites were widespread in oceans and evolved into many forms. Different types are found in different rock layers, helping geologists to subdivide Mesozoic time. During the Mesozoic era, many new groups of organisms appeared, including birds and mammals. Dinosaurs lived on the land until they died out at the end of the era. In the sea, there were reptiles called plesiosaurs and ichthyosaurs.

## Mesozoic periods

Geologists have divided the Mesozoic era into three time periods: the Triassic period (lasting from 245 to 208 million years ago); the Jurassic period (208 to 144 million years ago); and the Cretaceous period (144 to 66.4 million years ago).

As well as limestones and other marine rocks, the Triassic period is known for deposits of red sandstones and pebble-rich layers. These red-beds were formed on land. In Triassic times (named because the rocks are of three main types), shallow seas covered much of what is now Europe and creatures evolved from their Paleozoic ancestors. The great coal-forming forests of the Paleozoic era disappeared and were replaced by new plants. The first mammals evolved at the end of the Triassic period.

The Jurassic period is named for the Jura mountains of Switzerland, where there are thick layers of limestone and shale that were formed at this time. Jurassic rocks are known for their fossils. Many of these are of sea creatures that lived in the warm seas and oceans. These covered areas that were land during the Triassic period. Ammonites, clams, brachiopods (marine shellfish), corals, and echinoderms (marine animals usually with hard, spiny skeletons) are commonly found in Jurassic rocks. The best known Jurassic fossils are of the land-living dinosaurs. Some grew to great size, others were small and ran quickly. Flying reptiles called pterosaurs (TER-uh-SAWRZ) glided over the landscape on their leathery wings, and giant crocodiles moved in the rivers. The Jurassic climate was warm and pine trees developed.

The final period of the Mesozoic era is the Cretaceous, named for the Latin word for chalk, *creta*. The thick layers of chalk that were deposited on the sea floor are made of millions of microscopic organisms called coccoliths. These rocks can be seen along the southeast coast of England. At this time, the sea level was high and about a third of today's land was submerged. The Cretaceous rocks contain fossils of creatures similar to those that lived in the Jurassic period. There were ammonites, echinoderms, and other sea creatures, along with land-living dinosaurs. The Cretaceous climate was quite warm, and fossils of tender plants have been found near the South Pole. Modern flowering plants began to color the Cretaceous landscape and with them evolved the nectar-drinking insects.

At the end of the Mesozoic era, there was a devastating catastrophe. Many animals and plants died out. Nearly a quarter of all animal groups perished, including the dinosaurs. The exact reason for this is not clear, but there was widespread volcanic activity at the time that would have poured ash and dust into the sky and changed the climate. Also, there is evidence of a giant meteorite crashing into Earth near the Gulf of Mexico. This would have created devastating winds and tidal waves from the initial shock. The dust thrown into the atmosphere must have blotted out the sun for months, if not years, and so the climate cooled and the land was dark.

### CHECK THESE OUT!
✔CRETACEOUS PERIOD ✔GEOLOGIC TIMESCALE
✔JURASSIC PERIOD ✔TRIASSIC PERIOD

# Metal

**Shiny element that is a good conductor of heat and electricity**

More than 80 of the 100 or so known elements are metals. They are typically shiny silver-white or gray solids that conduct heat and electricity well. Metals have these properties because each atom in a sample of metal contributes some electrons to a pool of electrons that drifts around all of the atoms in the sample. This shared pool of electrons holds the atoms in the sample together and provides free-moving charged particles that can carry charge and heat energy. The free electrons vibrate in response to the incoming light wave and so generate a reflected wave. This accounts for the shiny appearance of metals.

Since the atoms in a sample of metal are not directly bonded to their neighbors, they can slip past each other as hammer blows, rollers, or tension cause the metal to change shape. This property makes metals suitable for forming into complex shapes, as in tools or other metal parts, and for stretching into wires. The hotter the metal, the more easily it changes shape. The bonding in metals also allows atoms of different elements to mix into alloys. These mixtures often have better properties than the pure metals.

## Alkali metals

The alkali metals are those that form group 1 (group IA) of the periodic table. In order of increasing atomic number, they are: lithium,

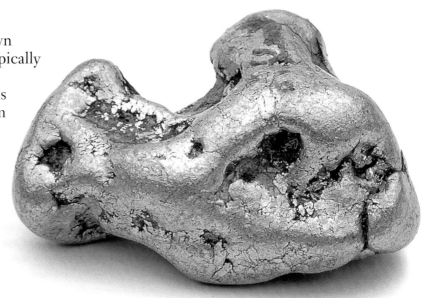

*Copper is found in various minerals. Natural nuggets of the metal, like this one, also exist.*

sodium, potassium, rubidium, cesium, and francium. They are all highly reactive elements, and their reactivity increases from lithium to francium. All react vigorously with water to form hydrogen and alkalis, or solutions of their basic hydroxides, which give the alkali metals their group name.

Alkali metals occur only as compounds in nature. They are so strongly bound in their compounds that they cannot be extracted by the chemical methods used to produce other metals. Instead, they are extracted by electrolysis (the use of an electrical current to cause a chemical change in a compound). The metals are soft enough to cut with a knife. They must be stored under oil to prevent them from reacting with substances in air. The alkali metals react rapidly with oxygen, water, and nonmetals such as sulfur and the halogens.

The most important of all the compounds of the alkali metals is sodium hydroxide, which is a vital raw material for the manufacture of soaps and numerous other chemical compounds. Washing soda is hydrated sodium carbonate ($Na_2CO_3.10H_2O$), and baking soda is sodium hydrogen carbonate ($NaHCO_3$; sodium

---

## HIGHLIGHTS

◆ Metals conduct heat and electricity well.

◆ The alkali metals form group 1 (group IA) of the periodic table.

◆ The alkaline earth metals form group 2 (group IIA) of the periodic table.

bicarbonate). Potassium nitrate ($KNO_3$) is used to make explosives. Lithium carbonate ($Li_2CO_3$) is used to treat some forms of mental illness.

## Alkaline earth metals

The alkaline earth metals form group 2 (group IIA) of the periodic table. In order of increasing atomic number, they are: beryllium, magnesium, calcium, strontium, barium, and radium. These elements are less reactive than the alkali metals, but more reactive than the transition metals. Their name dates from the 18th century, when chemists called their oxides "earths" because they were nonmetallic and unchanged by heat. They are called "alkaline" because their oxides react with water to produce basic hydroxides such as calcium hydroxide ($Ca(OH)_2$), although these hydroxides are much less soluble than those of the alkali metals.

Like alkali metals, alkaline earth metals only occur naturally as compounds. These compounds include limestone (calcium carbonate, $CaCO_3$) and dolomite (calcium magnesium carbonate, $CaCO_3.MgCO_3$). There are chemical methods for extracting the metals from their ores, but the most common method is electrolysis. The metals are silver-white solids that are much harder than the alkali metals, although the hardness decreases with increasing atomic number. Beryllium is hard enough to cut glass, and magnesium forms strong, lightweight alloys that are used to make automobile and aircraft parts. Barium and radium are much softer than the lighter metals.

The alkaline earth metals tarnish only slowly in air at room temperature, so they do not need to be stored under oil. When heated, the members of this group react with air, water, and nonmetals such as sulfur and the halogens. Each metal atom uses two electrons when it forms a compound. In most compounds, the electrons are transferred to other atoms as the alkaline earth metals form ions with a double positive charge. In a few of their compounds, beryllium and magnesium share their electrons in two covalent bonds with atoms of other elements.

Possibly the most important compound of an alkaline earth metal is lime (calcium oxide; $CaO$). Roasting limestone (calcium carbonate, $CaCO_3$) produces lime. Lime is an ingredient of cement and an important starting point for the manufacture of other calcium compounds. Calcium hydroxide ($Ca(OH)_2$), for example, is made by adding water to lime. It is used to treat wood pulp for making paper and to neutralize excess acidity in soil and water. Gypsum (hydrated calcium sulfate; $CaSO_4$) is a mineral that is used to make plaster of paris for treating fractured limbs. Magnesium is used mainly as the metal in alloys. Barium sulfate is used to provide contrast in X-ray examinations. When a patient drinks barium sulfate suspension before an X-ray examination, the liquid shows up the shape of the intestine on the X-ray scan.

Radium compounds are all radioactive. They were used in early studies of radioactivity and to make luminous paints that glowed in the dark. These paints are no longer used because of their hazardous radiation.

*This picture shows the industrial production of sheet metal. Metal is malleable—this means it can be easily hammered or rolled into thin sheets.*

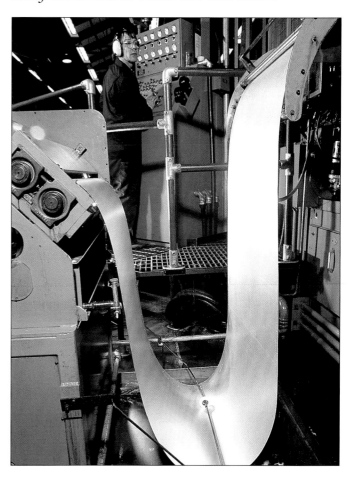

*This person is using a machine called a metal detector to search for metallic objects that are buried in the soil.*

## Transition metals

The transition metals are the elements that form groups 3 to 12 (groups IIIB to IIB) of the periodic table. With few exceptions, they are shiny silver-white solids. Copper and gold are orange and yellow solids. Mercury is a liquid at room temperature. They are less reactive than the alkali metals and alkaline earth metals. Many, such as copper, gold, chromium, and iron, are familiar from their use in everyday objects.

The transition elements form a bridge between the two main blocks of the periodic table. As atomic number increases from left to right across the block of transition elements, each element has one more electron than the element to its left. The additional electrons can take part in chemical reactions, which is why the transition metals can form compounds in which their oxidation number ranges from +1 to +8. Compounds with lower oxidation numbers usually contain ions, while those with higher oxidation numbers are molecular.

Many compounds of transition metals have bright colors, which change if the oxidation number increases or decreases. Potassium permanganate ($KMnO_4$) is a dark purple compound of manganese in oxidation state +7. It is able to oxidize (take electrons from) many other elements and compounds. As it does so, the manganese is reduced (gains electrons). On reduction, potassium permanganate forms compounds such as pale pink manganese (II) sulfate ($MnSO_4$) or black manganese (IV) oxide. The oxidation number of manganese in these compounds is +2 and +4.

The compounds of transition elements are used as catalysts (KA-tuhl-uhsts; substances that change the rate of chemical reactions without being changed themselves) in the chemical industry. Their ability to switch between oxidation states allows them to attach to reacting molecules and helps to weaken their bonds.

## Post-transition metals

The post-transition metals are a group of around 12 elements at the bottom-left corner of groups 13 to 16 (IIIA to VIA). The most important metals in this group are aluminum, tin, and lead. The post-transition metals are generally less reactive than other types of metals. They tend to form more molecular compounds than do metals of other classes. In this respect, the post-transition elements are similar to the metalloids on the border between metals and nonmetals in the periodic table.

***CHECK THESE OUT!***
✔METALLOID ✔METALLURGY

---

# EVERYDAY SCIENCE

### Reactivity Series

| | |
|---|---|
| 1. Potassium (K) | 8. Nickel (Ni) |
| 2. Calcium (Ca) | 9. Tin (Sn) |
| 3. Sodium (Na) | 10. Lead (Pb) |
| 4. Magnesium (Mg) | 11. Copper (Cu) |
| 5. Aluminum (Al) | 12. Mercury (Hg) |
| 6. Zinc (Zn) | 13. Silver (Ag) |
| 7. Iron (Fe) | 14. Gold (Au) |

The reactivity of an element is related to the vigor of its chemical reactions. The metals in the above list are in order of decreasing reactivity. Potassium reacts explosively with water, for example, but iron rusts slowly, and gold does not react at all with water. Metals toward the bottom of the table are easier to extract from their compounds than the more reactive metals. Gold, for example, occurs in nature as a free element. Iron can be extracted from its oxide by heating with carbon. Potassium can be extracted from its compounds only by electrolysis.

# Metalloid

In the periodic table, there are six stable elements that are not classed as metals or as nonmetals. These are boron, silicon, germanium, arsenic, selenium, and tellurium. These elements are called metalloids because they behave almost like metals. Astatine (AS-tuh-TEEN) may be another metalloid, but its extreme radioactive instability makes it impossible to collect a sample large enough to investigate.

## Boron

Boron belongs to the same group of the periodic table as aluminum—group 13 (IIIA)—but it behaves more like carbon. Pure boron is a poor electrical conductor that can form as extremely hard, transparent crystals. When it reacts with metals, it forms borides similar to the compounds that carbon forms with metals. Boron forms compounds with hydrogen that are similar to the hydrocarbons but much less stable. Diborane ($B_2H_4$) bursts into flames when it comes into contact with air.

## Silicon and germanium

Silicon is the most plentiful element in Earth's crust. It forms compounds with nonmetals just as carbon does. The structures of those compounds are often very different, however. While carbon dioxide is a simple molecule, silicon dioxide forms as huge, three-dimensional crystals with structures similar to diamond. Sand is a form of silicon dioxide. Pure silicon is a semiconductor, which is why it is used in computer chips. Germanium is also a member of group 14 (IVA) but is rarer than silicon and behaves more like a metal. Germanium was used in early semiconductor chips but has now been replaced by silicon.

## Arsenic and antimony

Arsenic and antimony are the next lightest members of group 15 (VA) after the nonmetals nitrogen and phosphorus. Each can be made in a gray form that has a metallic shine and conducts electricity. Both substances form compounds similar to those of the nonmetal phosphorus. One example is a poison called arsenic oxide ($As_2O_3$).

## Selenium and tellurium

Selenium and tellurium are the next lightest members of group 16 (group VIA) of the periodic table, after sulfur, which is a nonmetal. Most of their chemical properties are similar to those of sulfur. For example, they both form compounds that are similar to sulfuric acid and hydrogen sulfide. Both selenium and tellurium have unusual electrical properties. Selenium conducts poorly in the dark but better in light, which makes it useful for light-sensitive devices such as photographic exposure meters. Tellurium conducts better when it is hot, making it useful for heat-sensitive electrical devices.

### CHECK THESE OUT!
✔METAL ✔NONMETAL ✔PERIODIC TABLE

*Tellurium was discovered by Franz Muller in 1782. This metalloid element has eight natural isotopes (types) and nine radioactive isotopes.*

# Metallurgy

## The science of extracting and working metals and their alloys

Metals have hundreds of uses. They are essential for the construction of automobiles, ships, and airplanes. Metallurgy is the science and technology of separating metals from their ores, refining (purifying) them, and shaping them into useful objects. The science also includes the study of the properties of metals and the process of combining them into mixtures called alloys.

### Metallurgy in ancient times

Gold, silver, copper, and a few other metals occur naturally in a fairly pure state. They were the first metals to be known and worked by people. Most metals occur naturally as ores, in which the metal is combined with other elements such as oxygen or sulfur, to form oxides and sulfides.

Around 3000 B.C.E., archaeologists believed that humans first began to extract metals from their ores using heat. These people discovered that certain blue stones yielded copper when heated in a charcoal fire. Centuries later, people found that the ore chalcopyrite (KAL-ko-PY-RYT) also yielded copper. The metal that was produced contained impurities, however, and was brittle.

A fresh breakthrough came around 2000 B.C.E. Early humans discovered, probably by accident, that combining two metals could produce an alloy (metal mixture) that had useful properties.

Mixing two weak, soft metals (tin and copper), they produced a hard, strong alloy called bronze. The discovery brought about the dawn of a whole new age of technology and invention, now called the Bronze Age.

Bronze could be melted and cast in molds, which made it very useful. Similar methods for extracting iron from iron ore were also known, but early fires were not hot enough to melt iron. Instead, iron ore had to be hammered on stone anvils for a long time to squeeze the impurities out of the iron. Much later, metal workers discovered that iron became much harder if it was heated until red hot, and harder still if it was then doused with cold water to make an early form of steel. The secret of how to make steel

*For centuries, bronze has been used to make strong objects, such as this archaic Chinese vessel from the Shang dynasty (1400–1200 B.C.E.).*

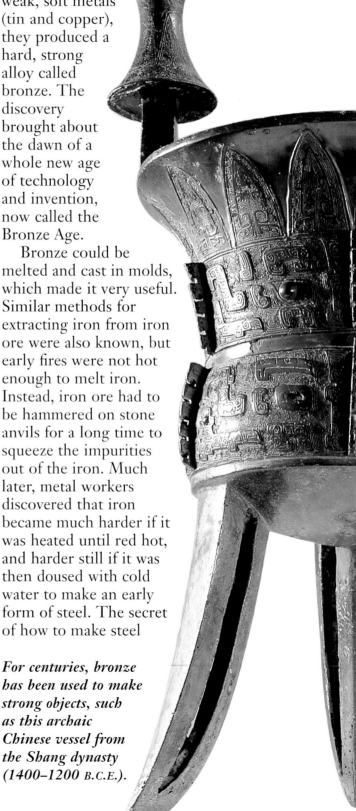

## HIGHLIGHTS

♦ Metallurgy is the science of obtaining metals from their ores, purifying them, and then working them into useful or decorative objects.

♦ Most metals do not exist in a pure state but as ores, in which state they are combined with other elements.

♦ There are three basic methods of extracting metals from their ores: smelting and roasting, leaching, and electrolysis.

weapons would have given some peoples a great advantage over their enemies.

Ancient peoples also knew of lead and mercury. Mercury oozed naturally out of volcanic rocks but was liquid and less useful. Lead could be extracted from its ores in a fire, but the metal obtained was soft, which meant it was useless for tools and weapons. Its dull gray color was a lot less attractive than silver or gold, so it was not used for making jewelry and other precious objects. However, it could be used to purify gold in a process called cupellation. Lead was later used to make weights. The Romans used it to make water pipes. Brass, another alloy of copper and tin, was discovered in early Roman times, around 500 B.C.E.

The next 1,500 years saw few major advances in the science of extracting and working metals. Then, in the 14th century, German metal workers learned to build blast furnaces, which could produce temperatures high enough to melt iron. A new age of metal working began.

## Extracting metals from ores

Some ores are so rich in metal that they do not need to be refined. Most, however, must be separated from the rock in which they are mixed. First, the rock is crushed to separate the different minerals, then the ore is extracted. Some iron, cobalt, and nickel ores are magnetic, so the metals can be attracted by a magnetic field. Other metals, such as gold, are much heavier than the rock with which they are mixed, so gold nuggets can be separated by a stream of water. In the days of the U.S. gold rushes, prospectors separated gold from river gravel by sluicing (SLOO-sing; washing) it in shallow pans. This technique was called panning.

In the early 20th century, a new technique called flotation developed from these methods. Flotation relies on the fact that some ores, particularly sulfides, are not easily wetted by water. When air is blown through a mixture of the crushed minerals in water, air bubbles attach themselves to the ore particles so that they float to the surface. This method is now used to process sulfides of copper, lead, and zinc.

Once the ore has been concentrated, the metal must be extracted using one of several methods, depending on the composition of the ore. Most ores are either oxides, sulfides, carbonates, or silicates. Iron, tin, and aluminum ores are oxides. Copper, lead, and zinc ores are mostly sulfides.

There are three basic methods of extracting metals from their ores. They may be processed either by being smelted or roasted in a very hot furnace, by leaching, or by electrolysis. Oxides are often worked through smelting (being heated to high temperatures with carbon). Sulfides are first roasted in air. Leaching involves dissolving the metal ore using acid or some other solvent (dissolving agent). This process is used for extracting copper, aluminum, and zinc. The technique of electrolysis involves passing an electric current through a molten or dissolved mixture of the ore. The current separates the metal from the ore.

Pure metals are obtained from the raw products of these extraction processes by refining. The simplest method is to oxidize the impurities. If the raw product is heated in a current of air, then impurities will combine with oxygen in the air and become oxidized, leaving the metal. This method is used to make high-quality steel from iron. Other metals are refined by electrolysis, producing pure copper, silver, nickel, gold, lead, and aluminum.

### CHECK THESE OUT!
✔ALLOY ✔COPPER ✔ELECTROLYSIS ✔IRON AND STEEL
✔METAL ✔MINING ✔ORE ✔REFINING ✔SMELTING

# Metamorphic Rock

**Rocks formed from preexisting rocks that have been changed by various processes**

Metamorphism means a change in form. Metamorphic rocks are made from already existing rocks. When rocks are heated or are under pressure deep underground, they are metamorphosed (changed). At great depths in the crust, there are hot fluids that can add new chemicals to rocks, and so change them. As rocks are buried deep underground by folding and mountain-building processes, so temperature and pressure increases. When temperatures rise above 300° to 400°F (150° to 200°C), metamorphism begins. Metamorphism ends when the rocks melt at around 1100° to 1400°F (600° to 750°C).

A mixture of eggs, flour, butter, and sugar can be baked in an oven to make a cake. When this is done, the overall chemical composition does not change. The ingredients blend and new textures form when heat is applied, and the result is a cake. The same type of effects are caused when rocks are metamorphosed. The new minerals and textures in metamorphic rocks are the result of how much heat and pressure the original rock has suffered.

The new crystals may be arranged along parallel bands in the rock, or clustered as spots. Eventually, after millions of years, erosion and weathering may unearth metamorphic rocks formed at great depth. By careful study of the minerals and their structures, geologists (scientists who study the structure and history of rocks) will be able to suggest the conditions under which the metamorphic rocks formed.

## Contact metamorphism

Heat is the cause of change in contact metamorphism. This type of metamorphism happens when a volcano erupts and red-hot lava pours over surface rocks and bakes them. It also happens at great depths when magma (molten rock) seeps among strata. Heat and fluids from the magma intrusion change the rocks nearby. A mass of magma may cover many cubic miles, and its heat can affect rocks over a wide area called the metamorphic aureole (AWR-ee-OHL). The area over which this type of metamorphism happens will depend on the size of the intrusion and its rock type. A large mass of magma many tens of miles across may have an aureole a mile or so wide. A small sheet of magma (a dyke or sill) may only metamorphose rocks for a few inches. If the intrusion is of granite magma, it

## HIGHLIGHTS

- ◆ Metamorphic rocks are made when rocks are recrystallized at high temperatures and pressure deep underground.

- ◆ Thermal or contact metamorphism happens when heat from magma or lava bakes nearby rocks.

- ◆ Dynamic metamorphism happens where huge faults in the crust move and grind rocks to dust.

- ◆ When meteorites and other extraterrestrial objects hit Earth, impact metamorphism can happen.

- ◆ Burial metamorphism changes sedimentary rocks at the bottom of a thick series of strata.

- ◆ Mountain-building metamorphism takes place when large areas of Earth's crust are subjected to raised temperature and pressure.

*A cut surface of marble, which is a type of metamorphic rock derived from limestone. Pure marble is white. The colors seen here are caused by impurities of other minerals.*

will affect the rocks over a wide area because this type of magma contains a lot of water, which seeps into the surrounding rocks. Other magmas are less wet and have a less widespread effect.

Rocks are recrystallized by the heat of magma intrusion. Limestone changes into the more compact rock marble, and sandstone recrystallizes into metaquartzite.

## Dynamic metamorphism

Earth's crust is always moving and cracking. The cracks are called faults, and rocks grind together here and break. The stress created when large faults move causes nearby rocks to be ground to dust. No high temperature is involved, but right on the fault plane, friction increases the temperature enough to recrystallize the ground-up fragments. The metamorphic rock formed is called mylonite (MY-luh-NYT).

## Impact metamorphism

If a comet or asteroid hits Earth, its impact causes very high temperatures and pressures. Molten droplets of shattered rock may be flung miles away from the impact crater. The metamorphic rock created is made of fused lumps of shattered and melted rock. Coesite (KOH-ZYT) is such a rock, which contains a mixture of high-pressure quartz (KWARTZ) and diamond. The meteor crater situated near Winslow in Arizona has these features.

## Burial metamorphism

Burial metamorphism happens where immense thicknesses of sediment have built up in a subsiding sea basin. There are no high temperatures, but pressure at the bottom of the pile of sediment may be moderate. The water trapped in the seabed sand and mud is squeezed out, and the layers may recrystallize. Mud may become slate. This rock is well known for its ability to split into very thin sheets and is used for roofing.

## Mountain-building metamorphism

Mountain-building metamorphism happens over very wide regions of Earth's crust. Movements of the crust caused by the immense forces of plate tectonics can drag rocks deep below ground where temperatures and pressures are extreme, especially when mountain building is taking place. Any type of rock—igneous, sedimentary, or already formed metamorphic rocks—can be caught up in these processes. Thousands of square miles of the crust may be affected, and deep in the roots of the new mountain chains metamorphic rocks such as gneiss (NYS) and schist (rocks containing parallel layers of flaky minerals, which split easily into thin leaves) are formed. Even granite can be altered into gneiss, so great are the temperatures and pressures. Granite is an igneous rock with a crystalline mosaic of minerals. Gneiss is a highly altered metamorphic rock characterized by alternating dark and light bands of minerals.

### CHECK THESE OUT!
✔IGNEOUS ROCK ✔PLATE TECTONICS ✔ROCK
✔SEDIMENTARY ROCK

# Meteor

**Streak of light that occurs as rock and dust from space enter Earth's atmosphere**

*This time-exposure image shows a Perseid meteor track (on the left) situated among many star trails.*

### Meteors and meteorites

Most meteors burn up about 55 miles (90 km) above Earth's surface. However, if the meteoroid is large or hard enough, it may not burn up altogether in the atmosphere. If it reaches Earth's surface, it is called a meteorite.

On average, almost one million meteors enter Earth's atmosphere every day. Most are no larger than a grain of sand. Scientists estimate, however, that the total weight of the tiny particles that fall to Earth amounts to 12,000 tons (10,700 tonnes) a year. On any night, the fiery trails of up to five meteors streak across the sky each hour. As they drop through the atmosphere, most of their rocky mass is burned away before it reaches Earth.

Sometimes enough of the meteoroid survives to gouge a large crater when it collides with Earth's surface. These hollows are called impact craters because they are caused by the impact as the meteorite strikes the ground. Crater Mound in Arizona is the site of a giant impact crater 4,000 feet (1,220 m) wide and 600 feet (180 m) deep. Scientists believe that this deep hollow was caused by a one-million-ton meteorite that crashed to Earth 50,000 years ago. Craters left by meteorites can also be seen on the surface of the Moon, as well as on planets such as Mars.

On the seabed of the Yucatán Basin, off Mexico's Yucatán Peninsula, scientists discovered a crater left by a giant meteorite that crashed to Earth at the end of the Cretaceous period. Scientists believe the impact of the meteorite raised a cloud of dust that spread around the world, blotting out sunlight for years. Some believe this event contributed to the extinction of the dinosaurs and other organisms that existed in prehistoric times.

On a clear night, a person may see dots of light suddenly streak across the sky. These are often called shooting stars, but they are not really stars. They are meteors, caused by meteoroids entering Earth's atmosphere.

Meteoroids are debris (duh-BREE; broken pieces) from comets, asteroids, and other celestial bodies. They are made of iron, stone, or a mixture of the two, and range from fine particles to giant rocks over a mile across, weighing 1,100 tons (1,000 tonnes).

Like the planets and their moons, meteoroids orbit the Sun. When a meteoroid's path leads it to collide with Earth, it enters this planet's atmosphere. Friction with the air produces intense heat and dazzling light. A streak of light—a meteor—is then seen from Earth.

## HIGHLIGHTS

◆ A meteor is a streak of light that a person sees from Earth when a meteoroid (piece of rock from space) enters Earth's atmosphere.

◆ A meteoroid that reaches the surface of Earth is called a meteorite.

At least one hundred other craters found around the world were caused by meteorites. The smallest meteoroids, less than 0.25 mm in diameter, also pass through Earth's atmosphere without melting. Since the 1970s, the National Aeronautics and Space Administration (NASA) has collected these particles, called interplanetary dust, from the lower atmosphere. The particles may help scientists understand the nature of the larger rock masses from which they came.

## Where do meteoroids come from?

Scientists believe meteoroids are debris from comets, asteroids, and other celestial bodies, including the Moon and Mars. Asteroids are chunks of rock and metal thought to be the remains of larger masses that have broken up in space collisions. Meteoroids formed of asteroid debris are ancient. They probably date back to the formation of Earth's Solar System, around 4.5 billion years ago, and may yield evidence of conditions at that time. Also, meteoroids from the Moon or Mars may help scientists to learn more about these bodies and how they formed.

*Meteor Crater in Arizona is thought to be about 25,000 years old.*

**LOOK CLOSER**

## Meteor Showers

Groups of meteors that appear to come from the same point in the sky are called meteor showers. The Perseids are probably the most spectacular meteor shower. They are seen during August and seem to radiate from a point in the constellation Perseus, near the W-shaped star group Cassiopeia (KA-see-uh-PEE-uh). The Perseids have been recorded since 811 C.E. Scientists believe they are ice and dust debris from the Comet Swift–Tuttle.

August is generally the best month for seeing meteor showers. In mid-month, the Cygnid meteors seem to come from the constellation Cygnus. The Lacertids and Andromedids are two more meteor showers that begin at the end of the month and continue into the fall.

Meteorites called SNC meteorites are probably from Mars. They are made of basalt, a dark, fine-grained volcanic rock, and were formed relatively recently. They were probably knocked off the planet's high volcanoes as other large meteorites collided with the surface.

# STORY OF SCIENCE

## Theories About Meteorites

During the 18th century, meteorites were a subject of argument. Many scientists were unwilling to believe they came from anywhere but Earth. German scientist Ernst Chladni (1756–1827) was among the first to suggest that meteorites were small pieces of former planets, but such ideas were generally scoffed at until the 1840s. Even after that date, many continued to question the idea that they came from space.

*An extensive collection of meteorites, fragments, and polished sections are on display here.*

Other meteoroids are chunks of rock and dust given off by comets as their orbit takes them near the Sun. Such debris is often concentrated near the path of the parent comet. Comet meteoroids produce meteor showers that occur regularly on certain dates and at predictable locations in the sky, and so are easy to spot. Meteor showers happen as Earth crosses the orbit of a comet and collides with the debris the comet has left behind. As the tiny particles of debris strike Earth's atmosphere at high speed, they ignite, producing streaks of light.

## What are meteoroids?

Scientists classify meteoroids according to the materials they contain. Some are made mostly of iron, others are stony, and others are a mixture of iron and stone. Iron meteoroids are dense. They are made up of 90 percent iron and 10 percent nickel. Stony–iron mixtures are fairly rare. They are made up of 50 percent iron, with the rest being mainly silicates (compounds of silicon and other minerals). Stony meteoroids are mostly silicates with 10 percent nickel and iron.

Most of the meteorites that fall to Earth are stony and similar to Earth's rocks. To be sure of a stony meteorite's origin, observers must have seen it fall. Scientists then find the impact site and perform detailed tests on the rock.

Many stony meteorites contain chondrules (KAHN-DROOLZ; small grains or crystals of cosmic minerals embedded in the stone). Such meteorites are called chondrites (KAHN-DRYTS). A small proportion of chondrites contain oxidized iron, chemically bound water (water that is combined with other elements and is not "free" water), carbon, and organic compounds from space, including amino acids. Some scientists believe that life on Earth may have begun when these basic building blocks of life were brought to a lifeless Earth by meteorites. At one time some people thought meteorites might contain fossils of life-forms from other planets.

## Meteorite finds

Evidence of meteorites is found around the world. Material from meteors has even been recovered from the oceans. During the 1970s, scientists discovered that Antarctica was a rich source of meteorites. There is little natural rock that is not covered by a thick sheet of ice on this vast, frozen continent, so rocks found scattered on the inland plains are likely to be meteorites.

Modern technology has made it easier to find meteorites. Meteor trails in the atmosphere can now be tracked by radar to lead researchers to fresh meteorite falls.

The 20th century saw a number of famous meteorite falls and finds. In 1908, a large meteor streaked across the sky in central Siberia. It exploded 5 miles (8 km) above Earth, leaving no crater but sending shock waves around the world. All trees within an area of 400 square miles (1,000 sq km) were flattened. Fortunately, meteors of this size strike Earth only once or twice every 100 million years.

### CHECK THESE OUT!
✔ASTEROID ✔COMET ✔CRATER

# Glossary

**algae** (AL-JEE) Plantlike organisms that mostly live in water.

**aperture** (AP-uhr-CHOOR) Opening.

**aureole** (AWR-ee-OHL) Glowing ring around a bright object such as the Sun.

**bait** (BAYT) Something used to attract an animal into a trap or a fish onto a hook.

**blast furnace** furnace in which a blast of pressurized air is used to produce very high temperatures. Used to refine iron ore.

**Bronze Age** Period when humans first used bronze; around 4000 B.C.E. to 1000 B.C.E.

**core** Center of an object.

**crustacean** (KRUHS-TAY-shuhn) Shelled, aquatic animal such as a crab, lobster, or water flea.

**decompose** To decay and separate into parts.

**diameter** (dy-A-muh-tuhr) Length of a line between two points on the edge of a circle that always passes through the circle's center.

**domains** (doh-MAYNZ) Small areas of magnetization in a ferromagnetic (easily magnetized) substance.

**dormant** Showing no signs of activity for a time.

**echinoderms** (ih-KY-nuh-DUHRMZ) Group of marine animals with radial (round) symmetry, including starfish and sea urchins.

**fatty acids** Group of acids, many of which occur naturally in fats, waxes, and the oils that give flowers their smell.

**fiberglass** Strong, light material made from glass fibers mixed with plastic.

**filament** Thread of a conducting material that glows when an electric current passes through it.

**forensic science** The use of science to investigate crimes.

**free radicals** Groups of atoms that can exist freely for a short time.

**fulcrum** (FOOL-krum) Fixed point on which a lever turns.

**gear** Toothed wheel that is part of a larger piece of machinery.

**launch vehicle** Rocket used to launch (send into orbit) a satellite or spacecraft. It stays on the ground at takeoff.

**magnetosphere** Area around a large object in space that is dominated by the object's magnetic field.

**momentum** Force gained by motion; measured by the length of time needed to bring the object to rest.

**mortar** (MAWR-tuhr) Building material that is a mixture of cement, lime, sand, and water.

**paralysis** (puh-RAH-luh-suhs) Inability to move.

**patent** (PA-tuhnt) Official document showing ownership of an idea or invention.

**payload** The cargo carried by a spacecraft.

**periscope** (PEH-ruh-SKOHP) Tube-shaped instrument containing lenses and mirrors that allows somebody to see around obstacles.

**pivot** (PIH-vuht) Pin on which something turns or balances.

**pulley** Rope over a grooved wheel; a heavy object can be lifted more easily by fastening it to the rope and pulling the other end.

**radius** Half a circle's diameter. *See also* diameter.

**solar panel** Sheet made up of cells that convert sunlight into electrical energy.

**splash down** When a crewed spacecraft arriving back on Earth splashes into the ocean.

**static electricity** Electricity produced by one-off, non-moving charges. For example, those produced by friction.

**synthetic** Humanmade; artificial.

# Index

Page numbers in **boldface type** refer to main articles and their illustrations. Page numbers in *italic type* refer to additional illustrations.

550
EXP
#6

Exploring Earth and Space
Science

| 05/06 | DATE DUE | |
|---|---|---|
| JAN 1 6 2007 | | |
| | | |
| | | |
| | | |
| | | |
| | | |
| | | |
| | | |
| | | |
| | | |
| | | |